The Thorvaldsen Museum

KØBENHAVN 1985

Catalogue edited by Bjarne Jørnæs and Anne Sophie Urne on the basis of
the catalogues in English (1961) and Danish (1975).
Translation by Ingeborg Nixon 1961. Revised by James Manley 1985.
Photos by Sophus Bengtsson, Jonals & Co., Ole Woldbye.
Printed by Poul Kristensens Bogtrykkeri, Herning.
Printer to the Royal Danish Court.
Grateful acknowledgements to *Konsul George Jorck og Hustru Emma Jorck's
Fond* for contributing to the publication of the catalogie.

Contents

On the cover: View of ground floor rooms. Photo: Keld Helmer-Petersen.

Plan of the Thorvaldsen Museum

Ground Floor
Entrance Hall and Corridors: Thorvaldsen's works (plaster models).
Rooms 1-21: Thorvaldsen's works (marble versions).
The Christ Hall: Plaster models for Thorvaldsen's works in the Church of Our Lady, Copenhagen.

First Floor
Corridors: Thorvaldsen's works (plaster models).
Rooms 22-31: Thorvaldsen's collection of paintings.
Room 33: Lecture Hall.
Rooms 35-40: Thorvaldsens's collection of antiquities.

Basement
Rooms 43-46: Thorvaldsens's clothes and personal relics. Sculptural technique.
Room 49 and Corridors 62 and 63: Thorvaldsen's juvenilia, sketch models and drawings.
Rooms 50-56: Exhibition Rooms.
Corridor 64: Plaster casts and antique sculptures. Photomontage with a presentation of Thorvaldsen's life and work.

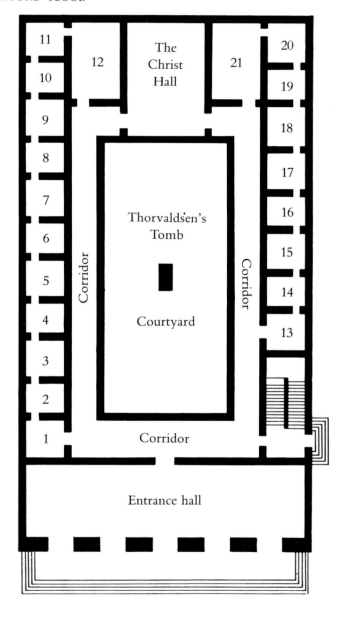

11
12
The Christ Hall
21
20

10
19

9
18

8
17

7
16

6
Corridor
Thorvaldsen's Tomb
Corridor
15

5
14

4
Courtyard
13

3

2

1
Corridor

Entrance hall

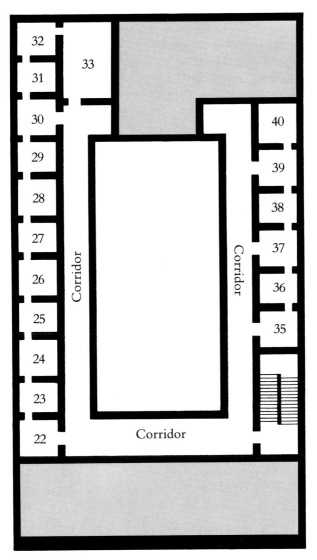

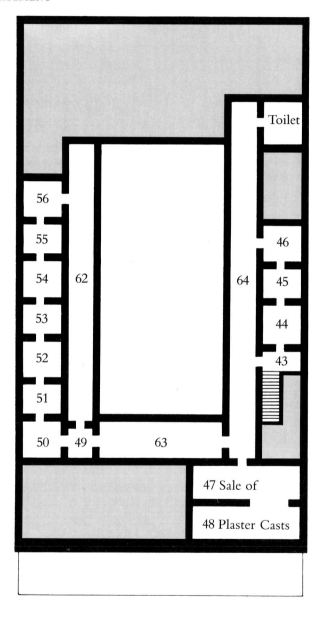

The Thorvaldsen Museum

is the property of the City of Copenhagen. The inscription on the
side of the building facing the palace church gives the following
account of its origin:

Thorvaldsen decided in the year 1837 in Rome that his works, collections and fortune should go to his native city Copenhagen and
that with them should be established a separate museum.

By means of contributions from King Frederik VI and King Christian VIII, from the City of Copenhagen and from fellow citizens of
every rank the task was completed 1848.

The building was designed by the architect M. G. Bindesbøll, and
erected under his direction. The work was begun in 1839. When the
building had already taken shape the desire was voiced that in addition to housing Thorvaldsen's works and collections it should also
be his final resting-place. When his consent had been given to this, a
sunken burial chamber was built under the centre of the courtyard,
decorated with white lilies on a blue ground. Thorvaldsen's coffin
was placed in it on September 6th 1848. The granite edging of the
tomb bears the following inscription:

BERTEL THORVALDSEN
b. 19th November 1770, d. 24th March 1844

During Thorvaldsen's lifetime the facades of the building were of
undecorated plaster. It was not until two years after his death that
Bindesbøll suggested that they should be ornamented with a frieze
of figures. The idea was Bindesbøll's; he is believed to have given
instructions for the subjects of the figure scenes, and how they were
to be placed on the walls. The composition and execution are the

work of Jørgen Sonne, under whose direction the frieze was made in 1846-48 and 1850. The technique used is unusual, the murals being constructed of tinted cement plaster applied direct to the walls.

The side facing the canal shows Thorvaldsen's arrival in Copenhagen in 1838. Facing the palace church is the frigate Rota, from which his works are being unloaded. The side facing the palace shows the transport of the works to the Museum. The decorations on the walls facing the courtyard were carried out during the summer and autumn of 1844. The bay-trees, oaks, and palms are the work of the landscape painter H. C. From, while the frieze with the chariot-driving genii is the work of the German sculptor Johann Scholl.

The bronze group above the main entrance – Victory reining in her horses – was presented by Christian VIII. It was modelled by H. W. Bissen, who used a sketch by Thorvaldsen for the figure of the goddess A 48, and one of his models for the second horse from the left A 125. The reliefs on the corner pilasters were carved in sandstone by Johann Scholl from models by H. E. Freund. They were originally partly painted.

For the ceiling decorations, which were inspired by antique models, Bindesbøll employed a number of artists and young academy students, of whom G. C. Hilker, Christen Købke, Jørgen Sonne and C. F. Sørensen are the best known. Bindesbøll was the moving spirit of the undertaking. His various helpers worked more or less independently under his leadership, and occasionally from his personal designs. His ability to guide and inspire them was legendary.

On September 17th 1848, the tenth anniversary of Thorvaldsen's return from Italy, the city council officially took over Thorvaldsen's art collections, and on the following day the Museum was opened to the public.

The Museum contains both Thorvaldsen's own works and his collections. The former consist of a large number of drawings, (some of which are exhibited in the basement), many sketch models, most of his original full-scale models, a number of casts, marbles made under his direction and finished by him, and marble copies made by various artists after his death.

Thorvaldsen's collections are very extensive, and provide interesting evidence of his wide artistic taste. They include works from ancient Egypt, antique glass, antique and oriental bronzes, Greek and Roman marbles, large collections of gems and coins, especially Greek, a fine collection of ancient vases, and various objects in terracotta. But the outstanding feature is the collection of paintings. Though it includes a few Renaissance paintings, the main emphasis is on the art of Thorvaldsen's own day, of which it gives an excellent impression. There are also important collections of watercolours, drawings, engravings, books, and casts of antique sculptures.

Thorvaldsen's Life

1770   Bertel Thorvaldsen born 19th November, son of Gotskalk
       Thorvaldsen, a woodcarver from Iceland, and Karen Dagnes
       from Jutland
1781   admitted to the Academy of Fine Arts, Copenhagen
1787   wins the Academy's Minor Silver Medal for a life drawing of
       a male nude
1789   wins the Academy's Major Silver Medal for the relief *Cupid
       Resting* (A756)
1791   wins the Academy's Minor Gold Medal for the relief
       Heliodorus Driven out of the Temple (A829)
1792   carves a wooden gateway relief, *Mounted Horseman* (A872)
       from a drawing by the Navy sculptor F. C. Willerup. Mod-
       els the relief *Hercules and Omphale* (A749) as a companion
       piece to a relief by Johann Gottfried Schadow
1793   wins the Academy's Major Gold Medal for the relief *The
       Apostles Peter and John Healing a Lame Man* (A830). During
       the period up to 1796 executes a number of portrait medal-
       lions and drawings.
1794   executes statues and reliefs (A757-758, Dep. 21-22) for Heir
       Presumptive Prince Frederik's palace at Amalienborg, from
       designs by N. A. Abildgaard, his teacher at the Academy
1795   wins the Academy's travelling scholarship. Models the bust
       of Prime Minister *A. P. Bernstorff* (A856)
1796   sails from Copenhagen 29th August, arrives 24th October in
       Malta
1797   leaves Malta 19th January, arrives in Naples via Palermo 1st
       February, and travels overland to Rome, arriving 8th March,
       a date later to be celebrated as Thorvaldsen's 'Roman birth-
       day'. Meets Georg Zoëga, a Danish archaeologist living in

Rome, finds a studio in the Via Babuino and reworks the bust of *A. P. Bernstorff* (A208)

1798   lives in the Via Sistina and forms a relationship with Anna Maria Uhden, née Magnani, married to the Prussian diplomat Wilhelm Uhden. Models the statuette *Bacchus and Ariadne* (A1)

1799   begins to copy antique sculpture in plaster (A54) and marble (A751, A759-761)

1800   starts work on a life-size statue of *Jason* (this clay model destroyed in 1802)

1801   models the statuette *Achilles and Penthesilea* (A777)

1802   starts work on a new statue of Jason, more than life-size (A52)

1803   finds a studio by the Piazza Barberini. *Jason* cast in plaster at the request of the poetess Friederike Brun and a marble version comissioned by Thomas Hope. Models the relief *Briseis Led away from Achilles by Agamemnon's Heralds* (A490)

1804   moves into the Casa Buti in the Via Sistina. Models the statues *Bacchus (A2) and Ganymede* (A41). Spends the summer with Baron and Baroness Schubart at Montenero and makes portrait busts of them (A718-719). Becomes a member of the Academy of Art, Florence

1805   appointed member of and professor at the Academy of Fine Arts, Copenhagen. Spends the summer at Montenero. Models the statue *Apollo* (A3) and starts work on the reliefs for a *Font* for Brahetrolleborg Church (A555)

1806   works on the *Font* and models the statues *Hebe* (A37) and *Psyche with the Jar of Beauty* (A26). His son with Anna Maria Magnani, Carlo Alberto, is born

1807   commissioned to do *four reliefs* for C. F. Hansen's Christiansborg Palace in Copenhagen and models the group *Cupid and Psyche Reunited in Heaven* (A28)

1808   models the statue *Adonis* (A53), commissioned in marble by Crown Prince Ludwig of Bavaria (later Ludwig I), and the reliefs *Hercules and Hebe* (A317), *Aesculapius and Hygieia* (A318) and possibly *Minerva and Prometheus* (A319) for Christiansborg Palace. Becomes a member of the Accademia di San Luca, the Roman academy of art, and carves, presumably for the occasion, the relief *A Genio Lumen* (A518)

1809 becomes executor of the estate of Georg Zoëga on the latter's death. Is commissioned to do *four statues* for the facade of Christiansborg Palace, a project only realized in Thorvaldsen's final years. Models the bust of *Ida Brun* (A218)

1810 models the last relief for Christiansborg Palace, *Jupiter and Nemesis* (A320), the relief *Caritas* ('Christian Love', A598), the *self-portrait bust* (A223), and presumably *Mars and Cupid* (A7), a reworking of a *Mars the Bringer of Peace* from 1808, now no longer extant.

1811 becomes a member of the art academies of Berlin and Milan. His son, Carlo Alberto, dies

1812 models the *Alexander Frieze* (A503) for the Quirinal Palace on the occasion of Napoleon's expected visit to Rome

1813 models two *Caryatids* (A55-56) for a monument to be erected in Warsaw commemorating Napoleon's alliance with Poland, later used for the Throne Room at Christiansborg Palace. Starts work on the statue of *Venus* (A12), completed in 1816. Elisa, his daughter with Anna Maria Magnani, born

1814 on the death of Baroness Schubart models a *tomb relief* (A618). Portrayed by C. W. Eckersberg (painting, Academy of Fine Arts, Copenhagen). Becomes a member of the Academy of Art, Munich

1815 models the statue of *Countess Osterman-Tolstoy* (A167) and the reliefs *Night* (A369), *Day* (A370) and *Priam Pleading with Achilles for the Body of Hector* (A492)

1816 starts work on the restoration of the antique pediment figures from Aegina for Ludwig of Bavaria, completed in 1817. Models the bust of *C. W. Eckersberg* (A224) and the statues *Ganymede Filling the Cup* (A43) and *Hebe* (A870)

1817 models the two statues of *Dancing Girls* (A178-179), *Ganymede with Jupiter's Eagle* (A45), *A Shepherd Boy* (A177) and the bust of *Lord Byron* (A257). Begins on *Cupid and the Graces* (A29), completed in 1819. Commissioned to do an equestrian statue of the Polish national hero Jozef Poniatowski

1818 models the statue *Mercury* (A5) and the portrait statue of

Princess Baryatinskaya (A172). Meets Miss Frances Mackenzie

1819   begins on preparations for the equestrian statue of *Poniatow-ski* (A249) and models the *Lucerne Lion* (A119). Becomes engaged to Miss Mackenzie, but breaks the engagement off shortly afterwards. Leaves Rome on the 14th of July and travels to Copenhagen by way of Switzerland, arriving on the 3rd of October. Starts on busts of the Danish Royal Family (A191-194)

1820   appointed titular Councillor of State. Works commissioned for the Church of Our Lady and Christiansborg Palace. Leaves Copenhagen on the 11th of August and travels through Poland, where the bust of *Alexander I* is modelled. Commissioned to do a monument to *Nicolaus Copernicus* (A113) and a tomb relief commemorating *Wlodzimierz Potoc-ki* (A115). Arrives in Rome on the 16th September

1821   models the *Christ* statue (A82) and begins on the *statues of the apostles* (A86-104) and the pediment group *The Preaching of John the Baptist* (A59-70) for the Church of Our Lady, Copenhagen

1822   works on the equestrian statue of *Poniatowski* (A125-126) and models *Copernicus* (A113)

1823   models the relief *Cupid Received by Anacreon* (A415). Commissioned to do a sepulchral monument to *Pius VII* for St. Peter's in Rome. Becomes a member of the French Academy of Art

1824   begins on the sculptures for the papal monument. Commissioned to do a sepulchral monument to *Eugène de Beauharnais,* Duke of Leuchtenberg, for the Michaelskirche in Munich, unveiled in 1830

1825   models a *Recumbent Lion* (A122)

1826   Vice-Presidency of the Accademia di San Luca. Visited by Pope Leo XII in his studio

1827   holds the office of President of the Accademia di San Luca until the end of 1828. Completes model for equestrian statue of *Poniatowski* (A123). Models sketches for a *Triumphant Muse* (A49-50), statue of Princess Caroline Amalie (A164) and presumably *Angel Holding a Font* (A112) for the Church of Our Lady

1828   completes *Jason* in marble (A822) for Thomas Hope, 25 years after its commissioning

1829   commissioned to do a monument to *Lord Byron*

1830   goes on a journey to Munich and is commissioned to do an equestrian statue of *Maximilian I, Elector of Bavaria,* and a statue of *Friedrich Schiller*

1831   completes the model for the statue of *Byron* (A130) and the marble version of *Adonis* for Ludwig of Bavaria. Sepulchral monument to *Pius VII* unveiled in St. Peter's

1832   adopts his daughter Elisa and goes with her on a journey to Vicenza. Continues alone to Milan. Commissioned to do a statue of *Johann Gutenberg* for Mainz. His daughter marries Colonel Fritz Paulsen

1833   appointed Director of the Academy of Art in Copenhagen. Begins modelling *Maximilian I* (A128), completed in 1835, and delegates the realization of a sketch for *Gutenberg* (A117), to be modelled full-size by H. W. Bissen (A114). Portrayed by Horace Vernet

1834   plans for a Thorvaldsen Museum discussed in Copenhagen

1835   models a sketch for *Schiller* (A138), modelled in colossal size (A770) by Wilhelm Matthiä

1836   models the series of reliefs *The Ages of Man and the Seasons* (A642-645) and a statue of *Conradin* (A150). Receives a Medal of Honour from the Accademia de San Luca

1837   decides to will his works and collections to Copenhagen. A committee is set up in Copenhagen for the estabilishment of the Thorvaldsen Museum, and a collection is begun for this purpose. M. G. Bindesbøll works on designs for the Museum. Thorvaldsen given honorary citizenship of Mainz. Models statue of a *Young Girl Dancing* (A181) during a cholera epidemic in Rome and starts on sketches for *three series of reliefs* (A458-479, A 433-448 and A 532-547), which are modelled by Pietro Galli for the Palazzo Torlonia and completed in 1838. Negotiations begun about a *Goethe* monument in Frankfurt

1838   models the statue *Vulcan* (A9). Sails from Italy on the 8th of August with the frigate *Rota,* carrying a large portion of

Thorvaldsen's works and collections. Appointed *Konferens-raad* (an eminent honorary title). Arrives in Copenhagen on the 17th September and moves into the Academy Director's residence at Charlottenborg. Given freedom of the City of Copenhagen on the 21st November. On the 5th December issues the official document giving his collections to the City.

1839 meets Baron and Baroness Stampe and models the bust of *Adam Oehlenschläger (A226)* on their estate, Nysø, along with the *Self-portrait* statue (A162). The statues of Christ and ten apostles in marble versions are installed in the Church of Our Lady, Copenhagen. Once Frederik VI has donated the site for the Museum building, and several architects have sent in ideas, M. G. Bindesbøll's design is chosen, and the work of building is begun. Thorvaldsen receives the Grand Cross of the Order of the Dannebrog. Frederik VI dies

1840 models the statue of *Christian IV* for the latter's chapel in Roskilde Cathedral and *two reliefs* depicting family life at Nysø (A636-637). Sends off two sketches of *Goethe* (A139-40) to Frankfurt, but the commission is cancelled

1841 starts out on the 24th of May on a journey to Rome accompanied by the Stampe family, arriving on the 12th of September. Given honorary citizenship of Stuttgart. In Rome models sketches for two statues of apostles, *Thaddaeus* (A106-107) and *Andrew* (A109) for the Church of Our Lady, to substitute for two statues done earlier

1842 reworks *Cupid and the Graces* (A31) and models the statues of *Thaddaeus* (A105) and *Andrew* (A108) in full-size versions. Leaves Rome at the beginning of October and arrives in Copenhagen on the 24th October. Visits his museum during building operations

1843 models the colossal *Hercules* (A14) and sketches for the statues of *Minerva* (A17-18), *Nemesis* (A19-19a) and *Aesculapius* (A20-21), all four intended for the facade of Christiansborg Palace in bronze, and later placed in Prince Jørgen's Courtyard between Christiansborg and the Thorvaldsen Museum

1844   begins work on the bust of *Luther* (A188). Dies in the Royal Theatre on the 24th of March. Lies in state in the assembly hall of Charlottenborg, and the funeral service is held on the 30th of March in the Church of Our Lady

1848   Thorvaldsen's coffin is laid in the burial chamber in the Thorvaldsen Museum's courtyard on the 6th of September. The Museum is officially opened on the 17th of September, and opened to the public the next day

Catalogue

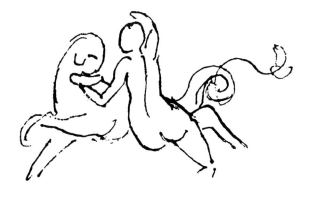

Catalogue of Thorvaldsen's Works

In the case of marbles known or believed to be executed under Thorvaldsen's direction, and possibly finished by him, his name has been added in brackets.

A1 Bacchus and Ariadne

Statuette. Original plaster model. Rome 1798. H. 58,4 cm.

A2 Bacchus

Statue. Original plaster model. Rome 1804. H. 140 cm.

A3 Apollo

Statue. Original plaster model. Rome 1805. H. 144 cm.

A4 Mercury about to Kill Argus

See A873.

A5 Mercury about to Kill Argus

Statue. Original plaster model. Rome 1818. H. 174,5 cm. Marble version, see A873.

A6 Mars and Cupid

Statue. Marble version of A7 (Rome, probably 1810) completed in 1862 by B. L. Bergslien under the supervision of H. W. Bissen. H. 247 cm.

A7 Mars and Cupid

Statue. Original plaster model, Cupid a plaster cast. Rome, probably 1810. H. 241 cm. An adapta-tion of a statue of Mars the Bringer of Peace, modelled in 1808, known from an engraving in Ferdinando Mori: *Le Statue e li Bassirilievi del Cavaliere Alberto Thorwaldsen,* Rome 1811. Marble version, see A6.

A8 Vulcan

Statue. Marble version of A9 (Rome 1838) completed in 1861 by B. L. Bergslien under the supervision of H. W. Bissen. H. 239 cm.

A9 Vulcan

Statue. Original plaster model. Rome 1838. H. 241 cm. Marble version, see A8.

A10 Vulcan

Sketch model for A9. Plaster. Rome, probably 1838. H. 60 cm.

A11 Venus with the Apple Awarded by Paris

See A853.

A12 Venus with the Apple Awarded by Paris

Statue. Original plaster model. Rome 1813-16. H. 161 cm. Marble version, see A853.

A13 Venus and Cupid

Statuette. Original plaster model.
Rome, probably about 1800.
H. 53,5 cm.

A14 Hercules

Statue. Original plaster model.
Copenhagen 1853. H. 388 cm. A
bronze cast in Prince Jørgen's
Courtyard at Christiansborg Palace,
Copenhagen.

A15 Hercules

Sketch model for A14. Plaster.
Copenhagen 1843. H. 67,5 cm.

A16 Hercules

First sketch model for A14. Plaster.
Copenhagen 1839. H. 59 cm.

A17 Minerva

Sketch model. Plaster. Copenhagen
1843. H. 70 cm. From this sketch
model H. W. Bissen modelled a colossal Minerva statue, a bronze cast
of which stands in Prince Jørgen's
Courtyard at Christiansborg Palace,
Copenhagen.

A18 Minerva

First sketch model for A17. Plaster.
Copenhagen 1839. H. 61 cm.

A19 Nemesis

Sketch model. Plaster. Copenhagen
1843. H. 66 cm. From this sketch
model H. W. Bissen modelled a colossal Nemesis statue, a bronze cast
of which stands in Prince Jørgen's
Courtyard at Christiansborg Palace,
Copenhagen.

A19a Nemesis

First sketch model for A19. Plaster.
Copenhagen 1839. H. 58 cm.

A20 Aesculapius

Sketch model. Plaster. Copenhagen
1843. H. 67,4 cm. From this sketch
model H. W. Bissen modelled a colossal Aesculapius statue, a bronze
cast of which stands in Prince
Jørgen's Courtyard at Christiansborg Palace, Copenhagen.

A21 Aesculapius

First sketch model for A20. Plaster.
Copenhagen 1839. H. 60 cm.

A22 Cupid Triumphant

Statue. Plaster cast. The original
plaster model, Rome 1814. H. 146
cm. Marble version, see A804.

A23 Cupid Triumphant, Examining his Arrow

Statue. Marble version of A24
(Rome 1823) executed 1845-54 by
J. Scholl. H. 145 cm.

A24 Cupid Triumphant, Examining his Arrow

Statue. Plaster cast. An adaptation
of A22. Rome 1823. H. 143,5 cm.
Marble version, see A23.

A25 Psyche with the Jar of Beauty

See A821.

A26 Psyche with the Jar of Beauty

Statue. Original plaster model.
Rome 1806. H. 131,7 cm. Marble
version, see A 821.

A27 Cupid and Psyche Reunited in Heaven

Statue. Marble version of A28
(Rome, probably 1807) executed in
1861 by Christian Freund under the
supervision of H. W. Bissen.
H. 135 cm.

A28 Cupid and Psyche Reunited in Heaven

Statue. Cupid a plaster cast, Psyche an original plaster model. Rome, probably 1807. H. 134,5 cm. Marble version, see A27.

A29 Cupid and the Graces

Statue. Original plaster model. Rome 1817-18. H. 171 cm. Marble version, see A894.

A30 The Graces

Sketch model for A29. Plaster. Rome 1817. H. 58 cm.

A31 The Graces with Cupid's Arrow, and Cupid Playing a Lyre

Statue. Marble version of A32 (Rome 1842) executed in 1864 by Christian Freund under the supervision of H. W. Bissen. H. 172,5 cm.

A32 The Graces with Cupid's Arrow, and Cupid Playing a Lyre

Statue. Plaster cast. An adaptation of A29. Rome 1842. H. 172,5 cm. Marble version, see A31.

A33 Cupid Playing a Lyre

Statue. Marble version of A786 (Rome 1819), probably executed in 1836 in Rome by J. Scholl. H. 58,6 cm.

A34 Cupid Playing a Lyre

See A786.

A35 Cupid Standing with his Bow

See A819.

A36 Cupid Standing with his Bow

Statue. Plaster cast. An adaptation of A173. Rome, probably 1819. H. 100,5 cm. Marble version, see A819.

A37 Hebe

Statue. Original plaster model. Rome 1816. H. 153 cm. Marble version, see A874. See also A870.

A38 Hebe

See A874.

A39 Hebe

Statue. Reworked plaster cast. Rome 1816. H. 153 cm. Marble version, see A874. See also A870.

A40 Ganymede Offering the Cup

See A854.

A41 Ganymede Offering the Cup

Statue. Plaster cast. The original plaster model, Rome 1804. H. 135,7 cm. Marble version, see A854.

A42 Ganymede Filling the Cup

Statue. Marble version (Thorvaldsen) of the original plaster model executed in 1816 in Rome. H. 135,5 cm. See A43.

A43 Ganymede Filling the Cup

Statue. Plaster cast. The original plaster model, Rome 1816. H. 135,7 cm. Marble version, See A42.

A44 Ganymede with Jupiter's Eagle

Statue. Marble version (Thorvaldsen) of the original plaster model executed in 1817 in Rome after a smaller version from 1815. H. 93,3 cm. W. 118,3 cm.

A45 Ganymede with Jupiter's Eagle

Statue. Plaster cast. The original plaster model, Rome 1817. H. 88,7 cm. W. 118,3 cm. Marble version, see A44.

A46 The Goddess of Hope

Statue. Marble version of A47 (Rome 1817) executed in 1859 by H. W. Bissen. H. 160,5 cm.

A47 The Goddess of Hope

Statue. Original plaster model. Rome 1817. H. 160,8 cm. Marble version, see A46.

A48 Victory on a Biga

Sketch model. Plaster. Rome 1827. H. 53,8 cm. After Thorvaldsen's death, H. W. Bissen modelled a Victory on a quadriga after this sketch model, a bronze cast of which was erected above the main entrance of the Thorvaldsen Museum.

A49 A Triumphant Muse and Cupid on a Biga

Sketch model. Plaster. Rome 1827. H. 65,5 cm.

A50 A Triumphant Muse and Cupid on a Biga

Sketch model. Plaster. Rome 1827. H. 71,3 cm.

A51 Jason with the Golden Fleece

Statue. Marble version of A52 (Rome 1802-03) executed in 1846-62 by B. L. Bergslien under the supervision of H. W. Bissen. Formerly in the Thorvaldsen Museum, now in the City Hall of Copenhagen. See A822.

A52 Jason with the Golden Fleece

Statue. Original plaster model. Rome 1802-03, reworked in the 1830's H. 245,5 cm. Marble versions, see A822 and A51.

A53 Adonis

Statue. Original plaster model. Rome 1808. H. 184,5 cm. Marble version, see A790.

A54 Pollux

Statue. Original plaster model. Rome 1799. H. 140 cm. Reduced copy of one of the Horse Tamers on the Quirinal Piazza (Monte Cavallo) in Rome.

A55 Caryatid

Statue. Plaster cast. The original plaster model, Rome 1813. H. 203,6 cm. Modelled for a projected monument in Warsaw to commemorate Napoleon's alliance with Poland. A marble version of the statue, placed in the throne room of Christiansborg Palace in Copenhagen i 1828, was destroyed in the palace fire of 1884.

A56 Caryatid

Statue. Plaster cast. The original plaster model, Rome 1813. H. 202,5 cm. Companion piece to A55. See also A735.

A57 The Erythraean Sibyl

Sketch model. Plaster. Inscribed: »ryth« (from Erythra). Copenhagen, probably 1820. H. 47,6 cm.

A58 The Cumaean Sibyl

Sketch model. Plaster. Inscribed: »ma« (from Cumae). Copenhagen, probably 1820. H. 49 cm.

A59 John the Baptist

Statue. Plaster cast. H. 239,7 cm. A59-A70 belong to a group modelled in 1821-22 in Rome for the pediment above the main entrance of the Church of Our Lady in Copenhagen. A copy in terracotta of the group was placed there in 1838, but was later replaced by a marble version, and finally in 1928 by bronze casts.

A60 Youth

Statue. Plaster cast. H. 162 cm. See A59.

A61 Father with his Son

Statue. Plaster cast. H. 186 cm. See A59.

A62 Mother with her Son

Statue. Plaster cast. H. 117,5 cm. See A59.

A63 Old Scribe

Statue. Original plaster model. H. 131 cm. See A59.

A64 Reclining Youth

Statue. Original plaster model. H. 92,2 cm. See A59.

A65 Standing Boy

Statue. Plaster cast. H. 150 cm. See A59.

A66 Pharisee

Statue. Original plaster model. H. 189,5 cm. See A59.

A67 Hunter

Statue. Plaster cast. H. 188 cm. See A59.

A68 Two Children

Statue. Original plaster model. H. 124,5 cm. See A59.

A69 Mother with her Child

Statue. Plaster cast. H. 132 cm. See A59.

A70 Reclining Shepherd

Statue. Original plaster model. H. 99 cm. See A59.

A71 Roman Warrior

Statue. Original plaster model. Rome 1820-21. H. 194 cm. Originally intended for the John the Baptist group A59-70.

A72 Seated Jew

Statue. Original plaster model. Rome 1820-21. H. 143 cm. Originally intended for the John the Baptist group A59-70.

A73 John the Baptist

Sketch model for A59. Plaster. Rome 1820-21. H. 49,7 cm.

A74. Youth

Sketch model for A60. Plaster.
Rome 1820-21. H. 41,3 cm.

A75 Mother with her Son

First sketch model for A62. Plaster.
Rome 1820-21. H. 29,7 cm. The
final sketch model for A62 is in the
Liebighaus in Frankfurt-on-Main.

A76 Boy with a Dog

Sketch model. Plaster. Rome 1820-
21. H. 17,5 cm. Originally intended
for the John the Baptist group A59-
A70, later replaced by A64.

A77 Mother with her Child

Sketch model for A69. Plaster.
Rome 1820-21. H. 32,3 cm.

A78 Mother with a Sleeping Child

First sketch model for A69. Plaster.
Rome 1820-21. H. 28,5 cm.

A79 Reclining Shepherd

Sketch model for A70. Plaster.
Rome 1820-21. H. 22 cm.

A80 Reclining Shepherd

First sketch model for A70. Plaster.
Rome 1820-21. H. 19,5 cm.

A81 Seated Man

Sketch model for A72. Plaster.
Rome 1820-21. H. 32 cm.

A82 Christ

Statue. Plaster cast of the original
plaster model, Rome 1821. H. 345
cm. A marble version was placed in
the Church of Our Lady, Copenhagen, in 1839.

A83 Christ

Statue. Preliminary version of A82.
Original plaster model. Rome 1821.
H. 141,5 cm. Probably modelled by
Pietro Tenerani under Thorvald-
sen's supervision.

A84 Christ

Sketch model for A82. Plaster.
Rome, probably 1821. H. 60 cm.
A preliminary anatomical sketch.

A85 Christ

Sketch model for A82. Plaster.
Rome, probably 1821. H. 55,7 cm.

A86 Peter

Statue. Original plaster model.
Rome 1821. H. 239 cm. A marble
version was placed in the Church of
Our Lady, Copenhagen, in 1839.

A87 Matthew

Statue. Original plaster model.
Rome 1822, H. 239,5 cm. A marble
version was placed in the Church of
Our Lady, Copenhagen, in 1839.

A88 Matthew

Sketch model for A87. Plaster.
Rome 1821. H. 47,1 cm.

A89 John

Statue. Original plaster model.
Rome 1824, H. 242 cm. A marble
version was placed in the Church of
Our Lady, Copenhagen, in 1839.

A90 John

Sketch model for A89. Plaster.
Rome 1821. H. 49,7 cm.

A91 James the Less

Statue. Original plaster model. Rome 1824. H. 238 cm. A marble version was placed in the Church of Our Lady, Copenhagen, in 1839.

A92 James the Less

Sketch model for A91. Plaster. Rome 1821-24. H. 51 cm.

A93 Philip

Statue. Original plaster model. Rome 1824. H. 234,5 cm. A marble version was placed in the Church of Our Lady, Copenhagen, in 1839.

A94 Jude (Thaddaeus)

Statue. Original plaster model executed in 1823 in Rome by Giuseppe Pacetti under Thorvaldsen's supervision and reworked in 1827. Later discarded by Thorvaldsen in favour of A105. H. 237 cm.

A95 Andrew

Statue. Original plaster model executed in 1823 in Rome by Joseph Hermann under Thorvaldsen's supervision. Later discarded by Thorvaldsen in favour of A108. H. 238 cm.

A96 Thomas

Statue. Original plaster model. Rome 1821. H. 240,5 cm. A marble version was placed in the Church of Our Lady, Copenhagen, in 1839.

A97 Thomas

Sketch model for A96. Plaster. Rome 1821. H. 52,3 cm.

A98 James the Greater

Statue. Original plaster model. Rome 1821. H. 238 cm. A marble version was placed in the Church of Our Lady, Copenhagen, in 1839.

A99 Bartholomew

Statue. Original plaster model. Rome 1824. H. 244 cm. A marble version was placed in the Church of Our Lady, Copenhagen, i 1839.

A100 Bartholomew

Sketch model for A99. Plaster. Rome 1824. H. 53,2 cm.

A101 Simon Zelotes

Statue. Original plaster model. Rome 1824. H. 241 cm. A marble version was placed in the Church of Our Lady, Copenhagen, in 1839.

A102 Simon Zelotes

Sketch model for A101. Plaster. Rome, beginning of the 1820's. H. 50 cm.

A103 Paul

Statue. Original plaster model. Rome 1821. H. 240,5 cm. A marble version was placed in the Church of Our Lady, Copenhagen, in 1839.

A104 Paul

Sketch model for A103. Plaster. Rome 1821. H. 50 cm.

A105 Jude (Thaddaeus)

Statue. Original plaster model executed in 1842 in Rome as a replacement for A94. H. 236 cm. A marble version was placed in the Church of Our Lady, Copenhagen, before 1848.

A106 Jude (Thaddaeus)

Sketch model for A105. Plaster.
Rome 1841. H. 79,2 cm.

A107 Jude (Thaddaeus)

First sketch model for A105. Plaster. Rome 1841. H. 71 cm.

A108 Andrew

Statue. Original plaster model executed 1842 in Rome as a replacement for A95. H. 241 cm. A marble version was placed in the Church of Our Lady, Copenhagen, before 1848.

A109 Andrew

Sketch model for A108. Plaster.
Rome 1841. H. 66,5 cm.

A110 Angel Standing with a Baptismal Font

Statue. Original plaster model.
Rome 1823. H. 180 cm. Created for the Church of Our Lady, Copenhagen, but replaced by the Kneeling Angel (see A112). A marble version in the Nationalmuseum, Stockholm.

A111 Angel Standing with a Baptismal Font

Sketch model for A110. Plaster.
Rome between 1820 and 1823.
H. 55,5 cm.

A112 Angel Kneeling with a Baptismal Font

Statue. Plaster cast. The original plaster model, Rome 1827 or 1828. H. 141,5 cm. A marble version was placed in the Church of Our Lady, Copenhagen, in 1839. See also A781.

A113 Nicolaus Copernicus

1473-1543. Astronomer.
Statue. Original plaster model.
Rome 1822. H. 277,2 cm. A bronze cast, erected in 1830 in Warsaw, was destroyed during the Second World War, but restored and re-erected in 1950.

A114 Johann Gutenberg

C. 1397-1468. The inventor of the art of printing.
Statue. Original plaster model executed in 1833-34 in Rome by H. W. Bissen under Thorvaldsen's direction and supervision. H. 348,5 cm. A bronze cast erected 1837 in Mainz.

A115 The Invention of the Movable Type

Relief for the base of the Gutenberg monument (see A114). Original plaster model executed in 1833-34 in Rome by H. W. Bissen under Thorvaldsen's direction and supervision. H. 90,5 cm. W. 118,5 cm. A bronze cast was placed on the monument in Mainz in 1837.

A116 The Invention of the Printing Press

Relief for the base of the Gutenberg monument (see A114). Original plaster model executed in 1833-34 in Rome by H. W. Bissen under Thorvaldsen's direction and supervision. H. 91 cm. W. 118,5 cm. A bronze cast was placed on the monument in Mainz in 1837.

A117 Johann Gutenberg

C. 1397-1468. The inventor of the art of printing.
Sketch model for A114. Plaster. Modelled in Rome in 1833 by H. W. Bissen under Thorvaldsen's direction. H. 54 cm.

A118 The Invention of the Printing Press

Sketch model for A116. Rome probably 1833. H. 40 cm. W. 51,5 cm.

A119 Dying Lion Protecting the Royal Arms of France (The Lucerne Lion)

Statue. Plaster cast. The original plaster model, Rome 1819. H. 84 cm. W. 161 cm. Cut in colossal size by Lucas Ahorn in the side of a cliff at Lucerne in memory of the Swiss Guards who fell in Paris during the Terror in 1792; completed in 1821.

A120 Monument to Karl Philipp von Schwarzenberg

1771-1820. Austrian prince and general, Duke of Krumau.
Sketch model for unexecuted monument. Plaster. Rome 1821. H. 97 cm.

A121 Recumbent Lion

Statue. Marble version (Thorvaldsen) of A122 (Rome 1825). H. 88 cm. Probably intended for the projected monument to Karl Philipp von Schwarzenberg (see A120).

A122 Recumbent Lion

Statue. Original plaster model. Rome 1825. H. 87,5 cm. Marble version, see A121.

A123 Jozef Poniatowski

1763-1813. Polish prince and general.
Equestrian statue. Original plaster model. Rome 1826-27. H. 463 cm. The statue was commissioned in 1817 and the final contract signed in 1820. Cast in bronze, it was to have been erected in Warsaw in 1832. This was forbidden by Emperor Nicholas I; he presented it to General Paskewitch, who erected it on his estate Gomel in the province of Mogilev in Russia. In 1921 it was restored to Warsaw, where it was erected in the Saxon Square in 1923. In 1944 it was blown up by the Nazi occupational forces before they abandoned the city. A new bronze statue, made after the original plaster model, was presented to the city of Warsaw by the Danish Government and the Corporation of Copenhagen, and unveiled in 1952.

A124 Jozef Poniatowski

1763-1813. Polish prince and general.
Equestrian statue. Partly an original plaster model. Rome 1826. Preliminary version of A123. H. 255 cm.

A125 Horse

Statue. Partly an original plaster model executed 1822-23 in Rome as a preliminary work for A123. H. 208,2 cm.

A126 Jozef Poniatowski

1763-1813. Polish prince and general.
Sketch model for A123. Plaster. Rome 1822. H. 82,5 cm.

A127 Maximilian I

1573-1651. Elector of Bavaria.
Sketch model for A128. Plaster.
Rome 1830-32. H. 80 cm.

A128 & A762 Maximilian I

1573-1651. Elector of Bavaria.
Equestrian statue. The horse (A128)
an original plaster model, Maximilian I (A762) a plaster cast, acquired
in 1855. Rome 1833-35. H. 522,5
cm. A bronze cast erected in 1839 in
Munich.

A129 Horse

Statue. Partly an original plaster
model executed in 1832-33 in Rome
as a preliminary work for A128.
H. 199 cm.

A130 Georg Gordon, Lord Byron

1788-1824. English poet.
Statue. Original plaster model.
Rome 1831. H. 174 cm. A first
model for the marble version in
Trinity College, Cambridge.

A131 The Genius of Poetry

Relief for the base of Lord Byron's
monument A130. Marble version of
A134 (Rome 1831). H. 80,2 cm.
W. 59 cm.

A132 Georg Gordon, Lord Byron

1788-1824. English poet.
Statue. Plaster cast, the head from
the bust A257 (Rome 1817), the rest
from the original plaster model
A130 (Rome 1831). H. 173,5 cm.
A marble version in Trinity College, Cambridge.

A133 George Gordon, Lord Byron

1788-1824. English poet.
Sketch model for A130. Plaster.
Rome 1830. H. 51,5 cm.

A134 The Genius of Poetry

Relief. Original plaster model.
Rome 1831. H. 79 cm. W. 60,5 cm.
Marble version, see A131.

A135 The Apotheosis of Schiller

Relief for the base of the Schiller
monument (see A770). Original
plaster model executed in 1837 in
Rome by Wilh. Matthiä after a
sketch by Thorvaldsen from 1835.
H. 62 cm. W. 127,5 cm. A bronze
cast placed 1839 on the monument
in Stuttgart.

A136 The Genius of Poetry

Relief for the base of the Schiller
monument (see A770). Original
plaster model executed in 1837 in
Rome by Wilh. Matthiä after a
sketch by Thorvaldsen from 1835.
See also A526. H. 84,5 cm. W. 88,3
cm. A bronze cast placed 1839 on
the monument in Stuttgart.

A137 The Goddess of Victory

Relief for the base of the Schiller
monument (see A770). Original
plaster model executed in 1837 in
Rome by Wilh. Matthiä after a
sketch by Thorvaldsen from 1835.
H. 84,5 cm. W. 88,5 cm. A bronze
cast placed 1839 on the monument
in Stuttgart.

A138 Friedrich Schiller

1759-1805. German poet.
Sketch model for A770. Plaster cast.
Rome 1835. H. 83,5 cm.

A139 Johann Wolfgang Goethe

1749-1832. German poet.
Sketch model for a projected monument in Frankfurt-on-Main of the
poet seated. Plaster cast. Copenhagen, probably 1839. H. 45,5 cm.

A140 Johann Wolfgang Goethe

1749-1832. German poet.
Sketch model for a projected monument in Frankfurt of the poet stand-
ing. Plaster. Copenhagen, probably
1840. H. 69,5 cm.

A141 Frederik VI

1768-1839. King of Denmark 1808.
Sketch model for a projected monument. Plaster. Copenhagen, December 1839. H. 45 cm.

A142 Pius VII

1742-1823. Gregorio Barnaba
Chiaramonti. Pope 1800.
Statue. Original plaster model.
Rome 1824-25. H. 295,3 cm. A
marble version was placed on the
monument to Pius VII in Saint Peter's in Rome, unveiled in 1831.

A143 Heavenly Wisdom

Statue. Original plaster model.
Rome 1825. H. 290,5 cm. A marble
version was placed on the monument to Pius VII in Saint Peter's in
Rome, uneveiled 1831.

A144 Divine Power

Statue. Original plaster model.
Rome 1825. H. 304,5 cm. A marble
version was placed on the monument to Pius VII in Saint Peter's in
Rome, unveiled 1831.

A145 The Coat of Arms of Pius VII Held by Two Angels

Relief. Original plaster model.
Rome c. 1824-30. H. 67,5 cm.
W. 207,5 cm. A marble version was
placed on the monument to Pius VII
in Saint Peter's in Rome, unveiled
in 1831.

A146 Angel

Statue. Original plaster model.
Rome 1830. H. 141,5 cm. A marble
version was placed on the monument to Pius VII in Saint Peter's in
Rome, unveiled in 1831.

A147 Angel

Statue. Original plaster model.
Rome 1830. H. 147,5 cm. A marble
version was placed on the monument to Pius VII in Saint Peter's in
Rome, unveiled in 1831.

A148 Monument to Pope Pius VII

Sketch model for A142-A145. Plaster. Rome 1824. H. 107 cm.

A149 Pius VII

1742-1823. Gregorio Barnaba
Chiaramonti. Pope 1800.
Sketch model for A142. Plaster.
Rome 1824. H. 44 cm.

A150 Conradin

1252-1268. The last of the Hohen-
staufens.
Statue. Original plaster model.
Rome 1836. H. 212,3 cm. A marble
version was placed on Conradin's
tomb in the church of Santa Maria
del Carmine, Naples, in 1847.

A151 Conradin

1252-1268. The last of the Hohen-
staufens.
Sketch model for A150. Plaster.
Rome 1833. H. 53 cm.

A152 Christian IV

1577-1648. King of Denmark 1588.
Statue. Original plaster model.
Copenhagen 1840. H. 212,3 cm.
A bronze cast, executed by
J. B. Dalhoff, erected 1845 in the
Chapel of Christian IV in the
Cathedral of Roskilde.

A153 Three Genii

The motto of Christian IV: *Regna
firmat pietas*. Relief. Original plaster
model. Inscribed: »Nysø 25
Novembr 1842«. H. 56 cm. W. 78
cm. Originally intended for the
monument to Christian IV in the
Cathedral of Roskilde. See A152.

A155 Wlodzimierz Potocki

1789-1812. Polish count and
general.
Statue. Original plaster model.
Rome 1821. H. 215,2 cm. A marble
version was placed on the Count's
tomb in the Wawel Cathedral in
Cracow in 1832 (see also A626 and
A627). Another marble version,
A794, was executed for the
Museum.

A156 Eugène de Beauharnais

1781-1824. Duke of Leuchtenberg,
Napoleon I's stepson and Viceroy
of Italy.
Statue. Original plaster model.
Rome 1827. H. 275 cm. A marble
version was placed on the Duke's
tomb in the Church of Saint
Michael, Munich, in 1830.

A157 The Genii of Life and Death

Sketch model. Plaster. Rome, probably 1825. H. 41,4 cm. Pietro Tenerani modelled a group after this
sketch model in 1827, a marble version of which was placed on the
sepulchral monument to the Duke
of Leuchtenberg in 1830. See A156.

A158 The Genii of Life and Death beside a Meta

Sketch model. Plaster. Rome, probably between 1815 and 1819.
H. 82,5 cm.

A159 Kneeling Angel

Sketch model for a statue, probably
executed for the tomb of a daughter
of Daniel Jacobi in Lübeck. Plaster.
Nysø 1839. H. 43,7 cm.

A160 Martin Luther

1483-1546. German reformer.
Sketch model for a projected statue
for the vestibule of the Church of
Our Lady, Copenhagen. Plaster.
Rome, probably 1838. H. 68 cm.

A161 Philipp Melanchthon

1497-1560. German reformer.
Sketch model for a projected statue
for the vestibule of the Church of
Our Lady, Copenhagen. Plaster.
Rome, probably 1838. H. 67 cm.

A162 Bertel Thorvaldsen Leaning on the Statue of Hope

1770-1844. Self-portrait.
Statue. Plaster cast. The original plaster model, Nysø 1839. H. 198 cm. Marble version, see A771. For the Goddess of Hope, see A46.

A163 Bertel Thorvaldsen

1770-1844. Self-portrait.
Sketch model for A162. Plaster cast. Nysø 1839. H. 65 cm.

A164 Caroline Amalie

1796-1881. Princess, later Queen of Denmark, married to Christian Frederik (Christian VIII).
Statue. Original plaster model. Rome 1827. H. 175 cm.

A166 Yelizaveta Alexeyevna Osterman-Tolstoy

1779-1835. Russian countess.
Statue. Marble version of A167 (Rome 1815) executed 1863 by C. C. Olsen under the supervision of H. W. Bissen. H. 138 cm.

A167 Yelizaveta Alexeyevna Osterman-Tolstoy

1779-1835. Russian countess
Statue. Original plaster model. Rome 1815. H. 136 cm. Marble version, see A166.

A168 Seated Lady

Sketch model. Plaster. Rome, probably between 1815 and 1819. H. 44,3 cm.

A169 Seated Lady

Sketch model. Plaster. Rome, probably between 1815 and 1819. H. 42 cm.

A170 Seated Lady with a Boy

Sketch model. Plaster. Rome, probably between 1815 and 1819. H. 42 cm.

A171 Maria Fyodorovna Baryatinskaya

1793-1858. Née Keller, married to the Russian Prince Ivan Ivanovitch Baryatinsky.
Statue. Marble version (Thorvaldsen) of A172 (Rome 1818), executed c. 1819-25. H. 181 cm.

A172 Maria Fyodorovna Baryatinskaya

1793-1858. Née Keller, married to the Russian Prince Ivan Ivanovitch Baryatinsky.
Statue. Original plaster model. Rome 1818. H. 180 cm. Marble version, see A171.

A173 Georgiana Elizabeth Russell

C. 1810-1867. Daughter of John Russell, Duke of Bedford.
Statue. Plaster cast. The original plaster model, Rome 1815. H. 100,3 cm. Marble version, see A773.

A174 Jeanina Emilie Stampe as Psyche

1833-1861. Daughter of Baron Henrik Stampe and Baroness Christine Stampe.
Statue. Original plaster model. Inscribed: »Nysøe d:12 novb. 1840«. H. 105 cm.

A175 Pietro Alberto Paulsen as a Boy Hunter

1834-1921. Son of Fritz Paulsen and Elisa Paulsen, née Thorvaldsen, Thorvaldsen's grandson.
Sketch model. Plaster. Nysø 1843. H. 42,8 cm.

A176 Shepherd Boy

See A895.

A177 Shepherd Boy

Statue. Original plaster model. Rome 1817. H. 148,5 cm. Marble version, see A895.

A178 Dancing Girl

Statue. Original plaster model. Rome 1817. H. 175,5 cm.

A179 Dancing Girl

Statue. An adaptation of A178. Plaster cast. Rome, between 1817 and 1822. H. 174,5 cm.

A180 Young Dancing Girl

Statue. Marble version of A181 (Rome 1837) begun in Thorvaldsen's Roman studio and completed after his death. H. 151 cm.

A181 Young Dancing Girl

Statue. Original plaster model. Rome 1837. H. 146,5 cm. Marble version, see A180.

A182 Young Dancing Girl

Sketch model for A181. Plaster. Rome, probably 1837. H. 60 cm.

A184 Flower Girl

Sketch model. Plaster. H. 70 cm.

A185 Youth with a Dog

Sketch model. Plaster. H. 60 cm.

A186 Apollinaris of Ravenna

Died 75 A. D. (?) First bishop of Ravenna and martyr.
Bust. Original plaster model. Rome 1821. H. 97,5 cm.

A187 Leonardo Pisano, Fibonacci

C. 1170-c. 1240. Italian mathematician. `
Bust. Marble version (Thorvaldsen) of the original plaster model A722 executed in Rome between 1834 and 1838 for the Protomoteca Capitolina, but never placed. Inscribed: »Leonardo Pisano detto Fibonacci principe de' Matematici visse nel secolo XII«; on the sides: »Monsignor Girolamo Galanti pose« and »Alberto Thorvaldsen scolpi«. H. 72,7 cm.

A188 Martin Luther

1483-1546. German reformer. Unfinished bust. Original plaster model. Copenhagen 1844. H. 55,4 cm. Thorvaldsen's last work.

A189 Maximilian I

1573-1651. Elector of Bavaria. Bust. Preliminary work for A762 (see A128). Original plaster model. Rome 1831. H. 66,5 cm.

A190 Ludvig Holberg

1684-1754. Danish playwright, historian, and philosopher.
Bust. Plaster cast. The original plaster model A876, Nysø and Copenhagen 1839. H. 55,2 cm.

A191 Frederik VI

1768-1839. King of Denmark from 1808.
Bust. Plaster cast. The original plaster model, Copenhagen 1819-20. H. 71,2 cm. Marble version, see A859.

A192 Marie Sophie Frederikke

1767-1852. Queen of Denmark, married to Frederik VI.
Bust. Original plaster model. Copenhagen 1819-20. H. 75 cm. Marble version, see A860.

A193 Caroline

1793-1881. Danish princess, daughter of Frederik VI.
Bust. Original plaster model. Copenhagen 1819-20. H. 71,8 cm. Marble version, see A857.

A194 Vilhelmine Marie

1808-1891. Danish princess, daughter of Frederik VI.
Bust. Original plaster model. Copenhagen 1819-20. H. 46,4 cm.

A195 Vilhelmine Marie

1808-1891. Danish princess, daughter of Frederik VI.
Bust. Marble version (Thorvaldsen) of A196 (Rome 1828). H. 70,3 cm.

A196 Vilhelmine Marie

1808-1891. Danish princess, daughter of Frederik Vi.
Bust. Original plaster model. Rome 1828. H. 69,5 cm. Marble version, see A195.

A197 Christian Frederik

1786-1848. Danish prince, from 1839 King Christian VIII of Denmark.
Bust. Plaster cast. The original plaster model A753, Rome 1821. H. 58,8 cm.

A198 Caroline Amalie

1796-1881. Princess, later Queen of Denmark, married to Christian Frederik (Christian VIII).
Bust. Plaster cast. The original plaster model A716, Rome 1820-21. H. 53,3 cm. See also A754.

A199 Frederik Carl Christian

1808-1863. Danish prince, from 1848 King Frederik VII of Denmark.
Bust. Original plaster model. Copenhagen 1820. H. 43,4 cm. A marble version belongs to Rosenborg Castle, see Dep. 33.

A200 Frederik Carl Christian

1808-1863. Danish prince, from 1848 King Frederik VII of Denmark.
Bust. Marble version (Thorvaldsen) of the original plaster model executed 1828 in Rome. H. 67,6 cm.

A201 Friedrich Wilhelm Carl Ludwig

1786-1834. Prince of Hessen-Philippsthal-Barchfeld.
Bust. Plaster cast. The original plaster model, Rome 1822. H. 61,6 cm.

A202 Juliane Sophie

1788-1850. Danish princess, daughter of Heir-Presumptive Prince Frederik, married to Prince Friedrich Wilhelm of Hessen-Philippsthal-Barchfeld.
Bust. Plaster cast. The original plaster model, Rome 1822. H. 60,6 cm.

A203 Christian Carl Friedrich August

1798-1869. Duke of Augustenborg.
Bust. Marble version (Thorvaldsen) of A204 (Rome 1819). H. 57 cm.

A204 Christian Carl Friedrich August

1798-1869. Duke of Augustenborg.
Bust. Original plaster model. Rome 1819. H. 55 cm. Marble version, see A203.

A205 Friedrich August Emil

1800-1865. Prince of Augustenborg.
Bust. Marble version (Thorvaldsen) of A206 (Rome 1819). H. 70,5 cm.

A206 Friedrich August Emil

1800-1865. Prince of Augustenborg.
Bust. Original plaster model. Rome 1819. H. 69 cm. Marble version, see A205.

A207 Andreas Peter Bernstorff

1735-1797. Danish statesman and count.
Bust. Marble version (Thorvaldsen) of the original plaster model executed in 1804 in Rome. H. 47,9 cm. A colossal version, see A209.

A208 Andreas Peter Bernstorff

1735-1797. Danish statesman and count.
Bust. Reworked version of A856. Original plaster model. Rome 1797. H. 51,5 cm.

A209 Andreas Peter Bernstorff

1735-1797. Danish statesman and count.
Bust. Original plaster model. Rome 1804. H. 84,8 cm. Reduced marble version, see A207.

A210 Henrik Hielmstierne

1715-1780. Danish Titular Privy Councillor and art collector.
Bust, modelled after a plaster cast of a bust by Hartman Beeken and a drawing after a painting by Jens Juel. Original plaster model. Rome, probably 1812. H. 53,7 cm.

A211 Conrad Rantzau-Breitenburg

1773-1845. Danish statesman and count.
Bust. Original plaster model. Rome 1805. H. 74,3 cm.

A212 Adam Gottlob Detlef Moltke of Nütschau

1765-1843. Danish count and poet.
Bust. Original plaster model. Rome 1803-04. H. 81,4 cm.

A213 Hans Holsten

1758-1849. Danish baron and admiral.
Bust. Original plaster model. Inscribed: »Den 17. Novemb. 1840«. Nysø. H. 56 cm.

A214 Conrad Danneskiold-Samsøe

1774-1823. Danish count and Lord Lieutenant.
Bust. Original plaster model.
Nordfeld 1820. H. 49,3 cm.

A215 Henriette Danneskiold-Samsøe

1776-1843. Née Kaas, married to Conrad Danneskiold-Samsøe.
Bust. Original plaster model. Inscribed: »A. Thorvaldsen Nysøe d. 6. December 1839«. H. 48,7 cm.

A216 Louise Danneskiold-Samsøe

1796-1867. Daughter of Conrad Danneskiold-Samsøe, 1820, married to Duke Christian of Augustenborg.
Bust. Original plaster model. Gisselfeld 1820. H. 49,9 cm.

A217 Christine Stampe

1797-1868. Danish baroness, née Dalgas, married to Baron Henrik Stampe.
Bust. Plaster cast. Inscribed: »Roma Maggio 1842« H. 57,4 cm.

A218 Ida Brun

1792-1857. Daughter of Constantin and Friederike Brun. Married Count Louis Philippe Bombelles, Austrian diplomat.
Bust. Original plaster model. Rome 1809. H. 57 cm. Marble version, see A810.

A219 Herman Schubart

1756-1832. Danish baron and diplomat in Italy (Leghorn).
Bust. Marble version (Thorvaldsen) of A718 (Montenero 1804). H. 70,4 cm. See also A812.

A220 Jacoba Elisabeth Schubart

1765-1814. Née de Wieling, married to Baron Herman Schubart.
Bust. Marble version (Thorvaldsen) of A719 (Montenero 1804). H. 69,6 cm. See also A813.

A221 Frederik Siegfried Vogt

1777-1855. Danish diplomat and chargé d'affaires in Naples.
Bust. Marble version (Thorvaldsen) of A222 (Rome 1837). H. 62,3 cm.

A222 Frederik Siegfried Vogt

1777-1855. Danish diplomat and chargé d'affaires in Naples.
Bust. Original plaster model. Rome 1837. H. 60,5 cm. Marble version, see A221.

A223 Bertel Thorvaldsen

1770-1844. Self-portrait.
Bust. Plaster cast of the marble version (Thorvaldsen) in the Royal Academy of Fine Arts in Copenhagen. The original plaster model executed in 1810 in Rome. H. 73,5 cm.

A224 Christoffer Wilhelm Eckersberg

1783-1853. Danish painter.
Bust. Original plaster model. Inscribed: »Eckersberg Roma li 12 Maggio 1816«. H. 51 cm. Marble version, see A788.

A225 Tyge Rothe

1731-1795. Danish philosopher.
Bust. Marble version (Thorvaldsen)
of the original plaster model
executed in 1797 in Rome. Inscribed: »Tyge Rothe«. H. 45,5 cm.

A226 Adam Oehlenschläger

1779-1850. Danish poet.
Bust. Original plaster model. In-
scribed: »Nysøe den 29. Set. 1839«.
H. 54,1 cm.

A227 Caspar Bartholin

1782-1805. Danish Bachelor of
Laws.
Bust. Original plaster model.
Rome, probably 1818-19. H. 58,1
cm.

A228 Sophie Dorothea Høyer

C. 1743-1808. Née Heldvad, married to the Lutheran pastor Jens Offesen Høyer, and mother of the
painter C. F. Høyer.
Bust. Original plaster model. Rome
1809. H. 47,8 cm. Marble version,
see A763.

A229 Johan Christian Dahl

1788-1857. Norwegian painter.
Bust. Original plaster model. Rome
1821. H. 5l,8 cm.

A230 Jørgen von Cappelen Knudtzon

1784-1854. Norwegian merchant.
Bust. Original plaster model. Rome
1816. H. 57,7 cm.

A231 Hans Carl Knudtzon

1794-1821. Norwegian merchant.
Bust. Original plaster model. Rome
1816. H. 53,5 cm.

A232 Ludwig

1786-1868. Crown Prince, later
King Ludwig I of Bavaria 1825-48.
Bust. Marble version (Thorvaldsen)
of A233 (Rome 1818). H. 67,9 cm.

A233 Ludwig

1786-1868. Crown Prince, later
King Ludwig I of Bavaria 1825-48.
Bust. Original plaster model. Rome
1818. H. 68 cm. Marble version, see
A232.

A234 Clemens Metternich

1773-1859. Austrian statesman,
count, later prince.
Bust. Marble version (Thorvaldsen)
of A235 (Rome 1819). H. 61 cm.

A235 Clemens Metternich

1773-1859. Austrian statesman,
count, later prince.
Bust. Original plaster model. Rome
1819. H. 63,2 cm. Marble version,
see A234.

A236 Karl Philipp von Schwarzenberg

1771-1820. Austrian prince and
general, Duke of Krumau.
Bust. Original plaster model. Rome
1821. H. 54 cm.

A237 Wilhelm von Humboldt

1767-1835. German baron,
philologist, diplomat, and
statesman.
Bust. Original plaster model. Rome
1808. H. 53,5 cm.

A238 Alexandrine von Dietrichstein

1775-1847. Née Countess Sjuvalov, married to the Austrian Prince Franz Josef Johann von Dietrichstein.
Bust. Original plaster model. Rome c. 1810. H. 55,5 cm.

A239 Giovanna Nugent

1795-1854. Née Riario-Sforza, married to the Irish Count Laval Nugent-Westmeath.
Bust. Original plaster model. Naples, probably 1818. H. 56,1 cm.

A240 Christian August Tiedge

1752-1841. German poet.
Bust. Original plaster model. Rome c. 1805-06. H. 65 cm.

A241 Henri François Brandt

1789-1845. Swiss medal engraver.
Bust. Original plaster model. Rome, probably 1817. H. 55,2 cm.

A242 Conrad Hinrich Donner

1774-1854. Danish merchant in Altona.
Bust. Original plaster model. Copenhagen 1840. H. 57,1 cm.

A243 Aaron Elias von Eichthal

1747-1824. Bavarian Court Banker.
Bust. Original plaster model. Rome c. 1830-31. H. 53,6 cm.

A244 Mrs. von Krause

Probably the wife of Jacob von Krause, Austrian Consul General in St. Petersburg.
Bust. Original plaster model. Rome 1819. H. 55,2 cm.

A245 Karoline von Rehfues

1799-1892. Née von Meusebach, married to the German writer Philipp Joseph von Rehfues.
Bust. Original plaster model. Rome 1827. H. 53,2 cm. Marble version, see A861.

A246 Alexander I

1777-1825. Czar of Russia 1801.
Bust. Plaster cast. The original plaster model A715, Warsaw 1820. H. 67,6 cm.

A247 Helen of Russia

1807-1873. Née Princess of Württemberg, married to Mikhail Palovitch, Grand Duke of Russia.
Bust. Original plaster model. Rome 1829. H. 73 cm.

A248 Maria Alekseyevna Narishkin

1762-1822. Née Senyavina, married to Alexander Lvovitch Narishkin, Grand Chamberlain at the Russian Court.
Bust. Original plaster model. Rome c. 1815-16. H. 66 cm.

A249 Jozef Poniatowski

1763-1813. Polish prince and general.
Bust. Preliminary work for A123. Original plaster model. Rome 1819. H. 59,7 cm.

A250 Maria Fyodorovna Baryatinskaya

1793-1858. Née Keller, married to the Russian Prince Ivan Ivanovitch Baryatinsky.
Bust. Preliminary work for A171. Original plaster model. Rome 1818. H. 57,5 cm.

A251 Anna Potocka?

1776-1867. Née Tyszkiewicz, married to the Polish Count Aleksander Potocki.
Bust. Original plaster model. Rome c. 1814-16 or 1820? H. 57,3 cm.

A252 Napoleon I

1769-1821. Emperor of France 1804-14.
Bust. Plaster cast. The original plaster model A909, Rome c. 1830. H. 100 cm. Marble versions, see A732 and A867.

253 Horace Vernet

1789-1863. French painter.
Bust. Marble version in colossal size of A254 (Rome 1832), begun in 1834 in Rome, and completed in 1856 in Copenhagen under the supervision of H. W. Bissen. H. 110,5 cm.

A254 Horace Vernet

1789-1863. French painter.
Bust. Original plaster model. Rome 1832. H. 48,9 cm. Marble version, see A253.

A255 Sir Walter Scott

1771-1832. Scottish author.
Bust. Plaster cast. The original plaster model, Rome c. 1832. H. 73,6 cm.

A256 George Gordon, Lord Byron

1788-1824. English poet.
Bust. Marble version of A257 (Rome 1817). H. 65,3 cm.

A257 George Gordon, Lord Byron

1788-1824. English poet.
Bust. Original plaster model. Rome 1817. H. 66,9 cm. Marble version, see A256. See also A132.

A258 Thomas Maitland

1759-1824. Lord High Commissioner of the Ionian Islands.
Bust. Modelled after a plaster cast of a bust, probably by Paolo Prossalendi. Original plaster model. Rome 1818. H. 130,4 cm. In 1820 a bronze cast of the bust and of the relief A600 were placed on a monument on the Island of Zakynthos. The bust in bronze was lost during the Second World War.

A259 George Granville Leveson , Lord Gower

1786-1861. Later Duke of Sutherland.
Bust. Original plaster model. Rome 1817. H. 57,1 cm.

A260 Edward Pellew

1757-1833. English baron, later First Viscount Exmouth. Admiral.
Bust. Original plaster model. Rome 1814. H. 51,3 cm.

A261 William Cavendish, Lord Bentinck

1774-1839. 1803-07 Governor of Madras, later Envoy Extraordinary to the Sicilian Court.
Bust. Original plaster model. Rome 1815 or 1816. H. 49,9 cm.

A262 Alexander Baillie

1777-1855. Scottish, of the Baillies of Dochfour.
Bust. Original plaster model. Rome 1816. H. 59 cm.

A263 Edward Divett

C. 1777-1819. Squire of Bystock, Devon.
Bust. Original plaster model. Rome 1817. H. 64,5 cm.

A264 Louisa Hope

C. 1786-1851. Née de la Poer Beres-ford, married to Thomas Hope.
Bust. Original plaster model. Rome 1817. H. 58,3 cm. Marble version, see A824.

A265 Henry Thomas Hope

1808-1862. Son of Thomas and Louisa Hope.
Bust. Original plaster model. Rome c. 1822-23. H. 47,3 cm. Marble version, see A825.

A266 Henry Thomas Hope?

1808-1862. Son of Thomas and Louisa Hope.
Bust. Plaster cast. The original plaster model. Rome c. 1817. H. 46,4 cm.

A267 Mary Ann Montagu

1781-1862. Daughter of Armar Corry, Earl of Balmore. Married to George John Montagu, Earl of Sandwich.
Bust. Original plaster model. Rome 1816. H. 69,9 cm.

A268 Eliza, Lady Glenorchy

1803-1861. Née Baillie, married to John Campbell, Lord Glenorchy, later Marquis of Breadalbane.
Bust. Original plaster model. Rome c. 1829. H. 72 cm.

A269 Julia Potocka

C. 1760-1794. Née Lubomirska, married to the Polish Count Jan Potocki.
Bust. Original plaster model. Rom c. 1832-33. H. 67,2 cm.

A270 Pius VII

1742-1823. Gregorio Barnaba Chiaramonti. Pope from 1800.
Bust. Preliminary work for A142. Original plaster model. Rome 1824. H. 67,3 cm.

A271 Ercole Consalvi

1757-1824. Italian cardinal.
Bust. Original plaster model. Rome 1824. H. 73,9 cm. A marble version was placed on Consalvi's tomb in the Pantheon, Rome, in 1824.

A272 Giovanni-Battista Sommariva

C. 1750-1826. Italian count, politician, and art collector.
Bust. Marble version of A273 (Rome 1817 or 1818). H. 51,5 cm. See also A741.

A273. Giovanni-Battista Sommariva

C. 1750-1826. Italian count, politician, and art collector.
Bust. Original plaster model. Rome 1817 or 1818. H. 49 cm. Marble version, se A272 and A741.

A274 Giovanni-Battista Sommariva

C. 1750-1826. Italian count, politician, and art collector.
Bust. Original plaster model. Rome c. 1821. H. 54,6 cm.

A275 Georg Wilhelm Wilding

1790-1841. Married to Donna Catharina di Branciforte, became the Principe di Butera in 1814 after the death of his father-in-law.
Bust. Original plaster model. Rome 1815. H. 69,6 cm. Marble version, see A890.

A276 Catharina di Branciforte

1768-1824. Née Branciforte e Pignatelli, daughter of the Principe di Butera. Married 1812 to Georg Wilhelm Wilding. 1814 Principessa di Butera.
Bust. Original plaster model. Rome 1815. H. 70,5 cm. Marble version, see A891.

A277 Giovanni Raimondo Torlonia

1754-1829. Duke of Bracciano, Roman banker.
Bust. Plaster cast. The original plaster model, Rome 1829. H. 54,2 cm.

A278 Marianna Florenzi

1802-1870. Née Baccinetti, married to Marchese Ettore Florenzi.
Bust. Original plaster model. Rome 1828. H. 71,9 cm. Modelled at the order of King Ludwig I of Bavaria as a companion piece to his own bust A233. Marble version, see A727.

A279 Vittoria Caldoni

1807-? Italian model from Albano.
Bust. Original plaster model. Rome 1821. H. 53,2 cm. Marble version, see A886.

A280 Ghazi 'L-Din Haidar

Padishah of Oudh, King of Oudh 1819-27.
Bust. Original plaster model. Rome 1824. H. 82 cm. Marble version, see A887.

A281 Vincenzo Camuccini

1771-1844. Italian painter.
Bust. Marble version (Thorvaldsen) of A282 (Rome 1810). H. 56,2 cm.

A282 Vincenzo Camuccini

1771-1844. Italian painter.
Bust. Original plaster model. Rome 1810. H. 57,7 cm. Marble version, see A281.

A283 John Wyllie

?-1848. Scottish surgeon.
Bust. Original plaster model. Rome 1831. H. 73,5 cm.

A284 Unknown Man

Bust. Original plaster model. Rome, probably 1830's. H. 50,5 cm.

A285 Wriothesley Russell?

1804-1886. Lord Russell. Son of John Russell, sixth Duke of Bedford.
Bust. Original plaster model. Rome c. 1828. H. 50,9 cm.

A286 Charles James Patrick Mahon?

1800-1891. Irish politician.
Bust. Original plaster model. Rome c. 1832. H. 61,4 cm.

A287 Unknown Man

Bust. Original plaster model. Rome, probably 1830's. H. 50,3 cm.

A288 Yuri Aleksandrovitch Golovkin

1762-1846. Russian diplomat, Count.
Bust. Original plaster model. Rome 1819. H 54 cm.

A289 George Hilaro Barlow

1762-1848. Knighted 1803. Governor General of India 1805-07. Governor of Madras 1807-12.
Bust. Original plaster model. Rome 1828. H. 63,5 cm. Marble version, see A892.

A290 Karl von Seinsheim?

1784-1864. Bavarian count.
Bust. Original plaster model. Rome 1818. H. 55,2 cm.

A291 Arthur Potocki

1787-1832. Polish count.
Bust. Original plaster model. Rome 1829. H. 68 cm.

A292 Unknown Man

Bust. Original plaster model. Rome c. 1816-19. H. 54,4 cm.

A293 Nicolaus Esterhazy

1765-1833. Hungarian prince.
Bust. Original plaster model. Rome 1817. H. 53 cm.

A294 Henry Labouchère

1798-1869. British statesman, later first Baron Taunton.
Bust. Original plaster model. Rome 1828. H. 65,9 cm.

A295 Stanislaw Kossakowski

1795-1872. Polish count, secretary at the Russian Embassy in Rome 1819-27.
Bust. Original plaster model. Rome 1825. H. 58,8 cm. Marble version, see A706.

A296 Unknown Man

Bust. Original plaster model. Rome c. 1824-30. H. 60,1 cm.

A297 Francis Basset?

1747-1821. Baron de Dunstanville, English political writer.
Bust. Original plaster model. Rome 1818. H. 56 cm.

A298 Thomas Hope

1769-1831. English art collector and author.
Bust. Original plaster model. Rome 1817. H. 55,2 cm. Marble version, see A823.

A299 George Agar Ellis

1797-1833. English historical writer, later Baron Dover.
Bust. Original plaster model. Rome 1818. H. 50,6 cm.

A300 François Gabriel de Bray

1765-1832. French by birth, entered Bavarian Service as a diplomat. Bavarian Count.
Bust. Original plaster model. Rome c. 1818-19. H. 51,2 cm.

A301 Michael Coronini-Cronberg

1793-1876. Austrian count.
Bust. Original plaster model. Rome 1816. H. 55,5 cm.

A302 Ivan Vorontsov?

1790-1856. Russian count.
Bust. Original plaster model. Rome c. 1803-04. H. 53 cm.

A303 John Campbell?

1796-1862. Lord Glenorchy, later Marquis of Breadalbane, M. P.
Bust. Original plaster model. Rome c. 1829. H. 70,4 cm.

A304 Yevdokia Ivanovna Golitsyn

1780-1850. Russian princess.
Bust. Marble version (Thorvaldsen) of the original plaster model executed 1803-04 in Rome. H. 73,1 cm.

A305 Unknown Lady

Bust. Original plaster model. Rome c. 1827-38. H. 48,6 cm.

A306 Unknown Lady

Bust. Original plaster model. Rome c. 1816-19. H. 55 cm.

A307 Jane Craufurd

C. 1798-1884. Daughter of the Scottish Baronet James Gregan Craufurd.
Bust. Original plaster model. Rome 1818. H. 53,6 cm. Marble version, see A898.

A308 Anne Bingham?

C. 1796-1850. Daughter of Richard Bingham, Earl of Lucan.
Bust. Original plaster model. Rome c. 1816-17. H. 56,3 cm.

A309 Harriet Frances Pellew

1794-1849. Née Webster, married to the English admiral Sir Fleetwood Pellew.
Bust. Original plaster model. Rome 1817. H. 55 cm.

A310 Marie Louise Playdeux?

Mistress of Prince Nicolaus Esterhazy.
Bust. Original plaster model. Rome c. 1817-18. H. 55,3 cm.

A311 Elizabeth Vernon?

1795-1838. Daughter of Richard Bingham, Earl of Lucan. Married to George Granville Vernon. From 1830 Lady Harcourt.
Bust. Original plaster model. Rome c. 1816-17. H. 53,5 cm.

A312 Wilhelmine Benigna Biron

1781-1839. Duchess of Sagan.
Bust. Original plaster model. Rome
1818. H. 58 cm. See also A720 and
A811.

A313 Georgina Bingham?

1799-1849. Daughter of Richard
Bingham, Earl of Lucan.
Bust. Original plaster model. Rome
c. 1816-17. H. 53,5 cm.

A314 Unknown Child

Bust. Plaster cast. The original plaster model, Rome c. 1816-19. H. 45
cm.

A315 Georgiana Elizabeth Russell

C. 1810-1867. Daughter of John
Russell, sixth Duke of Bedford.
Bust. Preliminary work for A173.
Original plaster model. Rome 1815.
H. 42,2 cm.

A316 Jupiter Enthroned between Minerva and Nemesis

Relief. Sketch model. Plaster.
Rome, probably 1822. H. 113 cm.
W. 457 cm. Executed in terracotta
by G. Borup in colossal size and in
1847 placed in the pediment of the
main facade of Christiansborg
Palace in Copenhagen, destroyed
by fire in 1884.

A317 Hercules Receiving the Draught of Immortality from Hebe

An Allegory of Strength.
Relief. Original plaster model.
Rome 1808. D. 147,5 cm. A marble
version was placed on the facade of
Christiansborg Palace, Copenhagen, in 1825; it is now in the pas-
sageway, »Kongeporten«.

A318 Hygieia Feeding the Snake of Aesculapius

An Allegory of Health.
Relief. Original plaster model.
Rome 1808. D. 146,5 cm. A marble
version was placed on the facade of
Christiansborg Palace, Copenhagen, in 1825; now in the passage-
way »Kongeporten«.

A319 Minerva Grants a Soul to Mankind Created by Prometheus

An Allegory of Wisdom.
Relief. Original plaster model.
Rome 1807-08. D. 147 cm. A marble version was placed on the facade
of Christiansborg Palace, Copenhagen, in 1825; it is now in the pas-
sageway »Kongeporten«.

A320 Nemesis Recites the Deeds of Men to Jupiter

An Allegory of Justice.
Relief. Original plaster model.
Rome 1810. D. 147,5 cm. A marble
version was placed on the facade of
Christiansborg Palace, Copenhagen, in 1825; it is now in the pas-
sageway »Kongeporten«.

A321 Hercules Receiving the Draught of Immortality from Hebe

Relief. Marble version in reduced
size of A317 (Rome 1808). D. 81,5
cm.

A322 Hygieia Feeding the Snake of Aesculapius

Relief. Marble version in reduced size of A318. (Rome 1808). D. 80,5 cm.

A323 Minerva Grants a Soul to Mankind Created by Prometheus

Relief. Marble version in reduced size of A319 (Rome 1807-08.). D. 80,5 cm.

A324 Nemesis Recites the Deeds of Men to Jupiter

Relief. Marble version in reduced size of A320 (Rome 1810). D. 80,5 cm.

A325 Minerva

Relief. Original plaster model. Rome c. 1836. D. 64 cm.

A326 Apollo

Relief. Original plaster model. Rome c. 1836. D. 65,5 cm.

A327 The Genius of Light with Pegasus

Relief. Original plaster model. Rome c. 1836. D. 67,5 cm.

A328 Clio, Muse of History

Relief. Original plaster model. Rome c. 1836. D. 64 cm.

A329 Euterpe, Muse of Music

Relief. Original plaster model. Rome c. 1836. D. 64 cm.

A330 Thalia, Muse of Comedy

Relief. Original plaster model. Rome c. 1836. D. 64,5 cm.

A331 Melpomene, Muse of Tragedy

Relief. Original plaster model. Rome c. 1836. D. 64,5 cm.

A332 Terpsichore, Muse of Dancing

Relief. Original plaster model. Rome c. 1836. D. 64,5 cm.

A333 Erato, Muse of Lyric and Love Poetry

Relief. Original plaster model. Rome c. 1836. D. 64 cm.

A334 Polyhymnia, Muse of Religious Poetry

Relief. Original plaster model. Rome c. 1836. D. 64 cm.

A335 Urania, Muse of Astronomy

Relief. Original plaster model. Rome c. 1836. D. 64 cm.

A336 Calliope, Muse of Epic Poetry

Relief. Original plaster model. Rome c. 1836. D. 64 cm.

A337 Mnemosyne, Mother of the Muses, and Harpocrates

Relief. Original plaster model. Rome C. 1836. D. 64,5 cm.

A338 The Hovering Graces

Relief. Original plaster model. Rome c. 1836. D. 65,5 cm.

A339 The Procession to Parnassus

Apollo with Pegasus and the Genius of Light; the Graces and the Muses, accompanied by cupids; Homer led by the Genius of Poetry.
Relief. Original plaster model.
Rome 1832. H. 63,3 cm. W. 490,5 cm.

A340 The Dance of the Muses on Helicon

Apollo, the Muses, and the Graces.
Relief. Marble version of A341 (Rome 1816) executed by Christian Freund under the supervision of H. W. Bissen. H. 72,5 cm. W. 159 cm.

A341 The Dance of the Muses on Helicon

Apollo, the Muses, and the Graces.
Relief. Original plaster model.
Rome 1816. And adaptation of a relief modelled in 1804 at Montenero. H. 73,5 cm. W. 160 cm. Marble version, see A340. See also A705.

A342 The Muses of Tragedy and Comedy (Melpomene and Thalia)

Relief. Original plaster model.
Nysø 1843. D. 76 cm.

A343 Cupid Listening to the Song of Erato

Relief. Marble version of the original plaster model executed 1830 in Rome. D. 56,5 cm.

A344 Apollo among the Shepherds

Relief. Sketch model. Plaster.
Rome 1837. H. 30 cm. W. 177 cm.
An enlarged marble version was executed by Pietro Galli for the pediment of the Villa Carolina in Castel Gandolfo.

A345 Diana Beseeches Jupiter for Permission to Devote Herself to Hunting

Relief. Original plaster model. Inscribed: »Albert Thorvaldsen Nysøe d. 20. April 1840«. H. 71,5 cm. W. 81,5 cm.

A346 Mercury Brings the Infant Bacchus to Ino

Relief. Original plaster model. An adaptation of A347. Rome, probably 1809. H. 74,5 cm. W. 74 cm.

A347 Mercury Brings the Infant Bacchus to Ino

Relief. Original plaster model.
Rome 1809. H. 49,5 cm. W. 50,7 cm. Marble version, see A796.

A348 Venus Rising from the Foam

Relief. Original plaster model.
Rome 1809. H. 42,3 cm. W. 38,5 cm.

A349 The Abduction of Ganymede

Relief. Original plaster model.
Rome 1833. H. 25,5 cm. W. 20,3 cm.

A350 The Abduction of Ganymede

Relief. Original plaster model. Rome 1833. H. 33,5 cm. W. 47,5 cm.

A351 Hebe Gives Ganymede the Cup and Pitcher

Relief. Original plaster model. Rome 1833. H. 48,2 cm. W. 47 cm.

A352 Pan Teaching a Child Satyr to Play on a Reed Pipe

Relief. Marble version of A353 (Rome 1831). H. 46,5 cm. W. 78,3 cm.

A353 Pan Teaching a Child Satyr to Play on a Reed Pipe

Relief. Original plaster model. Rome 1831. H. 46,4 cm. W. 77,8 cm. Marble version, see A352.

A354 Bacchante and a Child Satyr

Relief. Marble version of A355 (Rome 1833). H. 46,5 cm. W. 78,3 cm.

A355 Bacchante and a Child Satyr

Relief. Original plaster model. Rome 1833. H. 47 cm. W. 78,8 cm. Marble version, see A354.

A356 Pan and a Hunting Nymph

Relief. Original plaster model. Rome c. 1838. H. 67,2 cm. W. 58,2 cm. Marble version, see A728.

A357 Satyr Dancing with a Bacchante

Relief. Original plaster model. Nysø 1840-41. H. 63,5 cm. W. 72 cm.

A358 Satyr Dancing with a Bacchante

Relief. Original plaster model. Nysø 1840-41. H. 65,7 cm. W. 74,5 cm.

A359 Victory Recording Deeds on a Shield

Relief. Marble version of A360 (Rome c. 1830). H. 81,2 cm. W. 62,5 cm.

A360 Victory Recording Deeds on a Shield

Relief. Original plaster model. Rome c. 1830. H. 81,5 cm. W. 63,5 cm. Originally modelled for a pedestal for the bust of Napoleon I (see A909), but never used. Marble version, see A359.

A361 Victory Seated with a Sword and Helmet

Relief. Partly an original plaster model. Rome 1830. H. 98 cm. W. 71,5 cm. Originally modelled for the pedestal of the Potocki monument (see A155), but never used.

A362 Victory Standing with a Shield and Palm

Relief. Original plaster model. Rome c. 1830. H. 90 cm. W. 63 cm. Originally modelled for the pedestal of the Potocki monument (see A155), but never used.

A363 Victory

Relief. Original plaster model.
Rome 1830. H. 97,2 cm. W. 65 cm.

A364 Nemesis in a Chariot, Attended by the Genii of Punishment and Reward

Relief. Original plaster model.
Rome 1834. H. 97 cm. W. 187,7
cm. A marble version was placed in
the Memorial Chapel of Julius My-
lius, in the Villa Vigoni by Lake
Como.

A365 The Fates with the Thread of Life

Relief. Marble version A366 (Rome
1833) executed 1864 by C. C. Olsen
under the supervision of H. W. Bissen. H. 122 cm, W. 181 cm.

A366 The Fates with the Thread of Life

Relief. Original plaster model.
Rome 1833. H. 71 cm. W. 106 cm.
Enlarged marble version, see A365.

A367 Night

See A901.

A368 Day

See A902.

A369 Night

Relief. Original plaster model.
Rome 1815. D. 75 cm. Marble version, see A901 and A905.

A370 Day

Relief. Original plaster model.
Rome 1815 (or an adaptation from
1817). D. 78 cm. Marble version,
see A902 and A906.

A371 Cupid Feeding Hygieia's Snake

Relief. Marble version of A372
(Rome 1837). H. 80 cm. W. 57 cm.

A372 Cupid Feeding Hygieia's Snake

Relief. Original plaster model.
Rome 1837. H. 76 cm. W. 55,5 cm.
Marble version, see A371.

A373 Hygieia Crowned by Cupid (Love and Health)

Relief. Original plaster model. Inscribed: »Nysøe d 24. April 1840«.
H. 60,2 cm. W. 63 cm.

A374 The Graces Dancing

Relief. Original plaster model.
H. 64 cm. W. 56 cm.

A375 The Graces with Cupid in Chains of Roses

Relief. Marble version of A376
(Rome 1831). H. 39 cm. W. 72 cm.

A376 The Graces with Cupid in Chains of Roses

Relief. Original plaster model.
Rome 1831. H. 37,3 cm. W. 71 cm.
Marble version, see A375.

A377 Cupid in Heaven, on Jupiter's Eagle, with the Thunderbolt

A377-A380 represent Cupid's
dominion over the Four Elements,
in this case Air.
Relief. Marble version of A381
(Rome 1828). H. 48,2 cm. W. 64
cm.

A378 Cupid on Earth, as the Lion Tamer, with Hercules' Club

A377-A380 represent Cupid's dominion over the Four Elements, in this case Earth.
Relief. Marble version of A382 (Rome 1828). H. 48,3 cm. W. 64,7 cm.

A379 Cupid at Sea, on a Dolphin, with Neptune's Trident

A377-A380 represent Cupid's dominion over the Four Elements, in this case Water.
Relief. Marble version of A383 (Rome 1828). H. 48,2 cm. W. 64,2 cm.

A380 Cupid in the Underworld, as the Tamer of Cerberus, with Pluto's Pitchfork

A377-A380 represent Cupid's dominion over the Four Elements, in this case Fire.
Relief. Marble version of A384 (Rome 1828). H. 48,7 cm. W. 64,5 cm.

A381 Cupid in Heaven, on Jupiter's Eagle, with the Thunderbolt

Relief. Original plaster model. Rome 1828. H. 49 cm. W. 67 cm. Marble version, see A377.

A382 Cupid on Earth, as the Lion Tamer, with Hercules' Club

Relief. Original plaster model. Rome 1828. H. 49,5 cm. W. 65,5 cm. Marble version, see A378.

A383 Cupid at Sea, on a Dolphin, with Neptune's Trident

Relief. Original plaster model. Rome 1828. H. 48,3 cm. W. 64,1 cm. Marble version, see A379.

A384 Cupid in the Underworld, as the Tamer of Cerberus, with Pluto's Pitchfork

Relief. Original plaster model. Rome 1828. H. 48,7 cm. W. 66,5 cm. Marble version, see A380.

A385 Cupid on Jupiter's Eagle

Relief. Preliminary work for A381. Original plaster model. Rome 1828. H. 51,5 cm. W. 65 cm.

A386 Cupid on Jupiter's Eagle

Relief. Preliminary work for A381. Original plaster model. Rome 1828. H. 48 cm. W. 62,2 cm.

A387 Cupid with the Tamed Lion

Relief. Preliminary work for A382. Original plaster model. Rome 1828. H. 42 cm. W. 62 cm. Marble version, see A729.

A388 Cupid with the Tamed Lion

Relief. Original plaster model. Rome 1809. H. 53 cm. W. 72,3 cm.

A389 Cupid Riding on a Lion

Relief. Marble version of the original plaster model executed in 1831 in Rome. H. 58 cm. W. 66 cm.

A390 Cupid Riding on a Lion

Relief. Plaster cast. The original plaster model. Rome 1831. H. 54 cm. W. 62,2 cm. Marble version, see A389.

A391 Cupid Writes the Laws of Jupiter

Relief. Marble version (Thorvaldsen) of A392 (Rome 1831). H. 46 cm. W. 68,5 cm.

A392 Cupid Writes the Laws of Jupiter

Relief. Original plaster model. Rome 1831. H. 44,2 cm. W. 67 cm. Marble version, see A391.

A393 Cupid Asks Jupiter and Juno that the Rose May Be Queen of Flowers.

Relief. Marble version of A394 (Rome 1831). H. 35 cm. W. 57 cm.

A394 Cupid Asks Jupiter and Juno that the Rose May Be Queen of Flowers

Relief. Original plaster model. Rome 1831. H. 33 cm. W. 55,5 cm. Marble version, see A393. See also A878.

A395 Cupid and Ganymede Playing at Dice

Relief. Marble version (Thorvaldsen) of the original plaster model executed 1831 in Rome. H. 42,5 cm. W. 63 cm.

A396 Cupid Caressing the Faithful Dog

Relief. Marble version of A399 (Rome 1831). H. 39 cm. W. 60 cm.

A397 Cupid Making a Net to Catch a Butterfly

Relief. Marble version of A398 (Rome 1831) H. 39 cm. W. 60 cm.

A398 Cupid Making a Net to Catch a Butterfly

Relief. Original plaster model. Rome 1831. H. 39,5 cm. W. 59,7 cm. Marble version, see A397.

A399 Cupid Caressing the Faithful Dog

Relief. Original plaster model. Rome 1831. H. 39,8 cm. W. 59 cm. Marble version, see A396.

A400 Cupid Sailing

Relief. Original plaster model. Rome 1831. H. 26 cm. W. 47 cm.

A401 Cupid Sailing

Relief. An adaptation of A400. Original plaster model. Rome 1831. H. 44,5 cm. W. 61,5 cm.

A402 Cupid Collecting Shells for a Necklace

Relief. Original plaster model. Rome 1831. H. 35,5 cm. W. 50 cm.

A403 Cupid Charms Flowers from Stony Ground

Relief. Original plaster model. Rome 1831. H. 38 cm. W. 52 cm.

A404 Cupid Sets Stone on Fire

Relief. Original plaster model. Rome 1831. H. 50 cm. W. 37,2 cm.

A405 Cupid Holding out a Rose, and Concealing Thistles

Relief. Original plaster model.
Rome 1837. H. 70 cm. W. 62,5 cm.

A406 Cupid Holding out a Rose, and Concealing Thistles

Relief. An adaptation of A405.
Original plaster model. Rome 1837.
H. 58,3 cm. W. 44 cm.

A407 Cupid and Bacchus

Relief. Marble version of A408,
(Rome 1810?), probably executed in
1824 in Rome. H. 54,7 cm. W. 89,7
cm.

A408 Cupid and Bacchus

Relief. Original plaster model.
Rome, probably 1810. H. 53 cm.
W. 83 cm. Marble version, see
A407.

A410 Cupid with a Swan and Boys Picking Fruit

An Allegory of Summer.
Relief. Marble version of A411
(Montenero 1810 or Rome 1811).
H. 53,3 cm. W. 69,3 cm.

A411 Cupid with a Swan and Boys picking Fruit

An Allegory of Summer.
Relief. Original plaster model.
Montenero 1810 or Rome 1811.
H. 52,2 cm. W. 69,5 cm. Marble
version, se A410.

A412 Cupid and the Youthful Bacchus Treading Grapes

An Allegory of Autumn.
Relief. Marble version of A413
(Montenero 1810 or Rome 1811).
H. 51,5 cm. W. 67 cm.

A413 Cupid and the Youthful Bacchus Treading Grapes

An Allegory of Autumn.
Relief. Original plaster model.
Montenero 1810 of Rome 1811.
H. 50 cm. W. 69 cm. Marble version, see A412.

A414 Cupid Received by Anacreon

See A827

A415 Cupid Received by Anacreon

An Allegory of Winter.
Relief. Plaster cast. The original
plaster model, Rome 1823. H. 49,5
cm. W. 67 cm. Marble versions, see
A416 and A827.

A416 Cupid Received by Anacreon

Relief. Marble. An adaptation of
A415. H. 54 cm. W. 90,3 cm.

A417 Cupid Stung by a Bee Complains to Venus

Relief. Marble version (Thorvaldsen) of A780 (Rome 1809). H. 49
cm. W. 53 cm.

A418 Cupid Stung by a Bee Complains to Venus

Relief. An adaptation of A780.
Original plaster model. H. 70,5 cm.
W. 61 cm.

A419 Cupid's Arrows Forged in Vulcan's Smithy

Relief. Original plaster model. Rome, probably 1810. H. 74,5 cm. W. 130,3 cm.

A420 Venus, Mars, and Cupid in the Smithy of Vulcan

Relief. An adaptation of A419. Plaster, Mars an original plaster model, the other figures plaster casts. Rome, probably 1814. H. 75,7 cm. W. 137 cm.

A421 Cupid Riding on a Swan

Relief. Original plaster model. Inscribed: »Nysøe d. 18 Novemb. 1840«. D. 77,5 cm.

A422 Cupid on a Swan

Relief. Original plaster model. Nysø 1840. H. 59 cm. W. 69,5 cm.

A423 Leda and the Swan

Relief. Original plaster model. Inscribed: »Nysøe d 3 Febru .. 1841«. H. 68,5 cm. W. 99,2 cm.

A424 Shepherdess with a Nest of Cupids

Relief. Marble version (Thorvaldsen) of A425 (Rome 1831). Inscribed: »Thorvaldsen fecit«. H. 59,8 cm. W. 58,5 cm.

A425 Shepherdess with a Nest of Cupids

Relief. Original plaster model. Rome 1831. H. 57,5 cm. W. 58 cm. Marble version, see A424.

A426 The Ages of Love

Relief. Marble version of the original plaster model executed in 1824 in Rome. H. 52 cm. W. 148 cm. See also A427 and A739.

A427 The Ages of Love

Relief. Sketch model. Plaster. Rome 1824. H. 40 cm. W. 123,5 cm. Marble version, see A426.

A428 Cupid Leaves the Bed of the Sleeping Psyche

Relief. Original plaster model. Nysø 1841. H. 50,5 cm. W. 60,5 cm.

A429 Psyche with the Lamp Approaches the Sleeping Cupid

Relief. Original plaster model. Nysø 1841. H. 52 cm. W. 63 cm.

A430 Cupid Revives the Swooning Psyche

Relief. Marble version of A431 (Montenero 1810). H. 57,5 cm. W. 90,5 cm. See also A865.

A431 Cupid Revives the Swooning Psyche

Relief. Original plaster model. Montenero 1810. H. 48,8 cm. W. 80 cm. Marble version, see A430 and A866.

A432 Psyche Carried to Heaven by Mercury

Relief. Original plaster model. D. 58 cm.

A433–A448 A series of reliefs representing the legend of Cupid and Psyche as told by Apuleius.

Reliefs. Plaster casts of reliefs modelled 1838 from Thorvaldsen's drawings by Pietro Galli for the now demolished Palazzo Torlonia, Rome. H. 26,5 cm. W. 22 cm.

A433 Venus Asking Cupid to Arouse Psyche's Love for some Worthless Being.

See above.

A434 Cupid Gazing at the Sleeping Psyche

See above.

A435 Psyche's Father Consulting the Oracle

See above.

A436 Zephyr and Psyche

See above.

A437 Cupid Approaching the Sleeping Psyche

See above.

A438 Cupid Leaving the Bed of the Sleeping Psyche

See above.

A439 Psyche and her Sisters

See above.

A440 Psyche Trying to Detain Cupid

See above.

A441 Psyche and Pan

See above.

A442 Venus Commanding Psyche to Fetch Water from the River Styx

See above.

A443 Jupiter's Eagle Bringing Psyche Water from the River Styx

See above.

A444 Psyche and Charon

See above.

A445 Psyche and Cerberus

See above.

A446 Cupid Reviving the Swooning Psyche

See above.

A447 Psyche Carried to Heaven by Mercury

See above.

A448 Psyche and Cupid Reunited

See above.

A449 Cupid and Psyche, or Goodbye to Nysø

Relief. Plaster cast. Inscribed (reversed): »Nysøe [d 24 May 1841]« The original plaster model, Nysø 1841. H. 38,5 cm. W. 38,5 cm.

A450 Cupid and Psyche

Relief. Original plaster model. Nysø 1840. H. 73 cm. W. 60 cm. See A805-08.

A451 Cupid and Hymen

Relief. Marble version of A452 (Nysø 1840), executed in 1842-44 in Thorvaldsen's studio in Rome. H. 75,3 cm. W. 61 cm.

A452 Cupid and Hymen

Relief. Original plaster model.
Nysø 1840. H. 73 cm. W. 59 cm.
Marble version, see A451.

A453 Cupid Garlands Hymen's Torches

Relief. Original plaster model.
Copenhagen 1840. D. 47,8 cm.

A454 Cupid and Hymen Spinning the Thread of Life

Relief. Marble version of A455
(Rome 1831), executed 1832–34.
H. 42,5 cm. W. 57 cm.

A455 Cupid and Hymen Spinning the Thread of Life

Relief. Original plaster model.
Rome 1831. H. 42 cm. W. 59 cm.
Marble version, see A454.

A456 Cupid's Swansong

Relief. Original plaster model.
Nysø 1843. D. 93,5 cm.

A457 Hymen

Relief. Plaster cast. The original
plaster model A731, Nysø 1843.
D. 94 cm.

A458–A479 A series of reliefs representing the Metamorphoses of Ovid

Reliefs. Plaster casts of reliefs modelled in 1838 from Thorvaldsen's drawings by Pietro Galli for the now demolished Palazzo Torlonia, Rome.

A458 The Flight of Latona

See above. H. 32,5 cm. W. 25,3 cm.

A459 Diana with her Hind

See above. H. 33,7 cm. W. 25 cm.

A460 Diana Surprised by Actaeon

See above. H. 33 cm. W. 24,6 cm.

A461 Actaeon Torn by his Dogs

See above. H. 32,8 cm. W. 25 cm.
See also A779.

A462 Diana Killing Orion

See above. H. 33,5 cm. W. 25 cm.

A463 Orion Dying

See above. H. 33 cm. W. 23,5 cm.

A464 Chione and Daedalion

See above. H. 33,5 cm. W. 25,3 cm.

A465 Cupid Leading Diana to Endymion

See above. H. 33 cm. W. 25 cm.

A466 Endymion Sleeping

See above. H. 32,5 cm. W. 24,8 cm.

A467 Nymph with Bow

See above, H. 33 cim. W. 24,5 cm.

A468 Nymph with Arrow

See above. H. 33,5 cm. W. 24,5 cm.

A469 Nymph and a Young Girl

See above. H. 33,4 cm. W. 24,7 cm.

A470 Nymph with Torch

See above. H. 34 cm. W. 24,4 cm.

A471 Hunting Nymph

See above. H. 33,5 cm. W. 24 cm.

A472 Callisto

See above. H. 33,4 cm. W. 24,8 cm.

A473 Atalanta
See above. H. 33 cm. W. 24,8 cm.

A474 Meleager and the Calydonian Boar
See above. H. 32,9 cm. W. 25,7 cm.

A475 Hero with a Slain Lion
See above. H. 34 cm. W. 24,2 cm.

A476 Adonis
See above. H. 34,4 cm. W. 24,8 cm.

A477 Narcissus and Cupid
See above. H. 32,5 cm. W. 24,2 cm.

A478 Apollo and Daphne
See above. H. 34,5 cm. W. 22,5 cm.

A479 Pan with Syrinx and Cupid
See above. H. 33,9 cm. W. 26,2 cm.

A480 The Centaur Nessus Embracing the Struggling Deianira
Relief. Marble version (Thorvaldsen) of A481 (Rome 1814). H. 103,5 cm. W. 127,5 cm.

A481 The Centaur Nessus Embracing the Struggling Deianira
Relief. Original plaster model. Rome 1814. H. 102 cm. W. 123 cm. Marble version, see A480.

A482 Hylas Stolen by the Water Nymphs
Relief. Marble version of A483 (Rome 1831). H. 40,7 cm. W. 76 cm.

A483 Hylas Stolen by the Water Nymphs
Relief. Original plaster model. Rome 1831. H. 40 cm. W. 76,5 cm. Marble version, see A482

A484 Hylas Stolen by the Water Nymphs
Relief. Marble version of A485. (Rome 1833). H. 68 cm. W. 109,5 cm.

A485 Hylas Stolen by the Water Nymphs
Relief. Original plaster model. Rome 1833. H. 65 cm. W. 108,5 cm. Marble version, see A484.

A486 Perseus on Pegasus Rescuing Andromeda
Relief. Plaster cast. The original plaster model A742, Nysø 1839. D. 75,5 cm.

A487 The Sea-Goddess Thetis Dipping her Son Achilles in the River Styx
Relief. Original plaster model. Rome 1837. H. 97,5 cm. W. 136 cm.

A488 The Centaur Chiron Teaching Achilles to Throw a Spear
Relief. Original plaster model. Rome 1837. H. 102 cm. W. 124 cm. Marble version, see A798.

A489 Briseis Led away from Achilles by Agamemnon's Heralds
Relief. Marble version of A490 (Rome 1803), executed 1865 by Christian Freund under the supervision of H. W. Bissen. H. 114 cm. W. 239 cm.

A490 Briseis Led away from Achilles by Agamemnon's Heralds

Relief. Original plaster model. Rome 1803. H. 116 cm. W. 236,5 cm. Marble version, see A489.

A491 Briseis Led away from Achilles by Agamemnon's Heralds

Relief. An adaptation of A490. Original plaster model. Rome 1837. H. 71 cm. W. 135 cm.

A492 Priam Pleads with Achilles for Hector's Body

Relief. Original plaster model. Rome 1815. H. 93,5 cm. W. 193,5 cm. Marble version, see A775.

A493 Achilles Binds the Wounds of Patroclus

Relief. Marble version of A494 (Rome 1837). D. 67,5 cm.

A494 Achilles Binds the Wounds of Patroclus

Relief. Original plaster model. Rome 1837. D. 64,7 cm. Marble version, see A493.

A495 Achilles with the Dying Amazon Penthesilea

Relief. Marble version of A496, (Rome 1837). D. 67 cm.

A496 Achilles with the Dying Amazon Penthesilea

Relief. Original plaster model. Rome 1837. D. 64,7 cm. Marble version, see A494.

A497 Minerva Awarding Ulysses the Arms of Achilles

Relief. Marble version of A498 (Rome 1831). Probably executed 1832-33. H. 65,5 cm. W. 121,5 cm.

A498 Minerva Awarding Ulysses the Arms of Achilles

Relief. Original plaster model. Rome 1831. H. 63,2 cm. W. 119,2 cm. Marble version, see A497.

A499 Hector with Paris and Helen

Relief. Original plaster model. Rome 1809. H. 69,7 cm. W. 93 cm. Marble version, see A774.

A500 Hector with Paris and Helen

Relief. Original plaster model. Rome 1837. H. 84 cm. W. 165 cm.

A501 Hector's Farewell to Andromache

Relief. Original plaster model. Rome 1836 or 1837. H. 92,5 cm. W. 182,3 cm. Marble version, see A776.

A502 Homer Singing for the People

Relief. Original plaster model. Rome 1836-37. H. 97,7 cm. W. 198 cm.

A503 Alexander the Great's Triumphal Entry into Babylon

Frieze. Plaster cast. The original plaster model executed in 1812 in Rome for the Quirinal Palace on the occasion of the expected arrival of Napoleon I. H. 106,5 cm. W. 3446 cm.

A504 Alexander the Great in his Triumphal Chariot Greeted by the Goddess of Peace

Relief. A variation of the central section of the Alexander Frieze A503. Original plaster model. Rome, probably 1818. H. 116,5 cm. W. 290,2 cm.

A505 Alexander the Great's Triumphal Entry into Babylon

Frieze, a variation of A503 (Rome 1812). Plaster cast. H. 111 cm. W. 4026 cm. A marble version was executed between 1818 and 1827 for Count Sommariva's villa by Lake Como (Villa Carlotta). There are slight differences between A505 and the marble version.

A506 Woman Letting a Boy Ride a Ram

Relief. Plaster cast. The original plaster model, Rome 1831. H. 110,5 cm. W. 126,5 cm. Modelled as an extension to the marble version of the Alexander Frieze at Christiansborg Palace in Copenhagen, partly destroyed by fire in 1884. See A831-50.

A507 Four Babylonians with Horses

Relief. Original plaster model. Rome 1831. H. 110,5 cm. W. 200 cm. Modelled as an extension to the marble version of the Alexander Frieze at Christiansborg Palace in Copenhagen, partly destroyed by fire in 1884. See A831-50.

A508 Alexander the Great's Triumphal Entry into Babylon

Frieze. Reduced marble version with alterations of A503 (Rome 1812), begun in 1822 by Pietro Galli. H. 55,5 cm. W. 2294,5 cm.

A509 Alexander the Great in his Triumphal Chariot

Relief, a variation of the central section of A508. Marble version, probably of A712. H. 58 cm. W. 110 cm.

A510 Trading-Post by the River

Relief. Original plaster model. H. 55,2 cm. W. 100,3 cm. Modelled as an extension to the Alexander Frieze and used in the marble version A508.

A511 Mother and her Children with Sheep

Relief. Plaster. Partly an original model. H. 55,2 cm. W. 116 cm. Modelled as an extension to the Alexander Frieze and used in the marble version A508.

A512 Youth Leading a Horse

Relief. Original plaster model. Rome, probably 1829. H. 55 cm. W. 65 cm. Modelled as an extension to the Alexander Frieze A508, but not used.

A513 Warrior Leading a Horse

Relief. Original plaster model. Rome 1831. H. 55 cm. W. 75 cm. Modelled as an extension to the Alexander Frieze A508, but not used.

A514 Alexander the Great Induced by Thais to Set Fire to Persepolis

Relief. Marble version of A515 (Rome 1832) executed in 1865 by B. L. Bergslien and C. C. Olsen under the supervision of H. W. Bissen. H. 95 cm. W. 198 cm.

A515 Alexander the Great Induced by Thais to Set Fire to Persepolis

Relief. Original plaster model. Rome 1832. H. 94 cm. W. 197,5 cm. Marble version, see A514.

A516 Alexander the Great Induced by Thais to Set Fire to Persepolis

Relief. An adaptation of A515. Original plaster model. Rome 1837. H. 83 cm. W. 197 cm.

A517 Art and the Light-bringing Genius: *A Genio Lumen*

Relief. Probably a preliminary work for A518. Original plaster model. Rome 1808 (?). H. 50,5 cm. W. 66,5 cm.

A518 Art and the Light-bringing Genius: *A Genio Lumen*

Relief. Original plaster model. Rome 1808. H. 103 cm. W. 136 cm. Marble version, see A828.

A519 The Genius of Light

Relief. Original plaster model. Nysø 1841. D. 31 cm. Designed for a medal, *Ingenio et Arti,* to be awarded to distinguished scientists and artists, instituted by Christian VIII.

A520 The Genius of Painting

Relief. Original plaster model. Inscribed: »Nysø d' 21 Juli 1843«. D. 93,5 cm.

A521 The Genius of Architecture

Relief. Original plaster model. Inscribed: »Nysø d' 3 Decemb. 1843«. D. 96 cm.

A522 The Genius of Sculpture

Relief. Original plaster model. Inscribed: »Nysø d ... Juli 1843«. D. 93 cm.

A523 The Genius of Sculpture

Relief. Original plaster model. Inscribed: »Kjøbenhavn d. 8 Marts 1844«. D. 94 cm.

A524 The Genius of Sculpture Seated on the Shoulder of the Statue of Jupiter

Chalk-sketch on a slate for a relief. Copenhagen 1844. H. 109 cm. W. 109 cm. Thorvaldsen's last sketch.

A525 The Genii of Painting, Architecture, and Sculpture

Relief. Original plaster model. Nysø 1843. D. 78 cm.

A526 The Genius of Poetry

Relief, the first version of the relief A136 for the base of the Schiller monument. Original plaster model. Rome 1835. H. 76 cm. W. 116 cm.

A527 The Genius of Poetry
Relief. Original plaster model. Inscribed: »Kjøbeha ... 24 Ap. 4«. (after Thorvaldsen's death). Copenhagen 1844. D. 97,5 cm.

A528 The Genii of Poetry and Harmony
Relief. Original plaster model. Inscribed: »Nysøe 30 Juli 1843«. D. 77,5 cm.

A529 The Genius of Peace and Freedom
Relief. Original plaster model. Copenhagen 1844. H. 75 cm. W. 190,5 cm.

A530 The Genius of Government
Relief, modelled for the equestrian statue of Maximilian I in Munich (see A128), but not used. Original plaster model. Rome 1837. H. 97,5 cm. W. 151,5 cm.

A531 The Genius of Justice
Relief, modelled for the equestrian statue of Maximilian I in Munich (see A128), but not used. Original plaster model Rome 1837. H. 97,2 cm. W. 154 cm.

A532-A545 A series of reliefs representing Genii of the Arts and Crafts
Reliefs. Plaster casts of reliefs modelled 1838 from Thorvaldsen's drawings by Pietro Galli for the now demolished Palazzo Torlonia, Rome. H. 27 cm. W. 19 cm.

A532 The Genius of Poetry
See above.

A533 The Genius of Tragedy
See above.

A534 The Genius of Comedy
See above.

A535 The genius of Music
See above.

A536 The Genius of Dancing
See above

A537 The Genius of Government
See above.

A538 The Genius of War
See above.

A539 The Genius of Navigation
See above.

A540 The Genius of Trade
Se above.

A541 The Genius of Medicine
See above.

A542 The Genius of Gardening
See above.

A543 The Genius of Agriculture
See above.

A544 The Genius of Astronomy
Se above.

A545 The Genius of Religion

See above.

A546 Seven Genii

The Genii of Architecture, Sculpture, Painting, Fishing, Hunting, Agriculture, and Gardening.
Relief. Plaster cast. H. 38,5 cm. W. 55,5 cm. See note above A532. For the last two genii, see also A543 and A542.

A547 Six Genii

The genii of Dancing, Government, War, Navigation, Trade (see A536-A540), and Justice.
Relief. Plaster cast. H. 36 cm. W. 53,5 cm. See note above A532.

A548 The Genius of the New Year

Relief. Plaster cast. The original plaster model, Nysø 1840. D. 57 cm.

A549 Justitia

Relief. Plaster cast. The original plaster model, Nysø 1841. H. 82,6 cm. W. 59 cm.

A550 Denmark Praying for the King

Relief. Design for a medal on the occasion of the accession of Christian VIII. Original plaster model. Inscribed: »Gud velsigne Kongen«. (God Save the King). Copenhagen 1839. D. 49 cm.

A551 Adam and Eve with Cain and Abel

Relief. Original plaster model. Rome 1838. H. 100 cm. W. 149 cm.

A552 Adam and Eve with Cain and Abel

Relief. Sketch model for A551. Plaster. Rome 1837 or 1838. H. 35 cm. W. 36,4 cm.

A553 Rebecca and Eliezer by the Well

Relief. Original plaster model. Inscribed: »Nysøe d. 26 Janua(r) 1841«. H. 94 cm. W. 183,3 cm.

A554 The Judgement of Solomon

Relief. Sketch model. Plaster. Rome 1835. H. 39,5 cm. W. 199 cm. Modelled for a projected relief for the pediment of the City Hall and Court House of Copenhagen.

A555 Baptismal Font

The reliefs of the four sides represent: The Baptism of Christ, The Virgin with Jesus and Saint John as Children, Christ Blessing the Children, and Three Hovering Angels, symbolizing Faith, Hope, and Charity.
Square font with reliefs. Original plaster model (except for the garland, which is a cast). Rome 1805-07. H. 77,8 cm. W. 72,5 cm. The first marble version in the church of Brahetrolleborg, Funen. Later marble versions in the Cathedral of Reykjavik, Iceland, and the Church of the Holy Ghost, Copenhagen.

A556 The Virgin with Jesus and Saint John as Children

Relief. A variation of the relief on A555. Original plaster model. Rome 1806. H. 57 cm. W. 52 cm.

A557 The Baptism of Christ

Relief. Plaster cast. The original plaster model, Copenhagen 1820. H. 95 cm. W. 223,5 cm. Marble version in the Church of Our Lady, Copenhagen. See also A730.

A558 The Institution of the Eucharist

Relief. Plaster cast. The original plaster model, Copenhagen 1820. H. 97,5 cm. W. 224 cm. Marble version in The Church of Our Lady, Copenhagen.

A559 Christ's Entry into Jerusalem

Frieze. Original plaster model. Nysø 1839-40. H. 64,2 cm. W. 747 cm. A preliminary work for the frieze above the main entrance of the Church of Our Lady, Copenhagen.

A560 Christ on the Road to Calvary

Frieze. Original plaster model. Nysø 1839-40. H. 66,5 cm. W. 758,5 cm. A preliminary work for the frieze in the choir of the Church of Our Lady, Copenhagen.

A561 The Resurrection of Christ

Sketch model. Plaster cast. The original plaster model, Rome 1835. H. 40 cm. W. 189,5 cm. Modelled for a projected relief for the pediment of the Palace Chapel in Copenhagen.

A562 Christ and the Two Disciples at Emmaus

Relief. Original plaster model. Rome 1818. H. 63 cm. W. 28,5 cm. Executed in silver for the tabernacle on the high altar of SS. Annunziata, Florence.

A563 Christ and the Two Disciples at Emmaus

Relief. Plaster cast, probably of a relief modelled 1839 at Nysø as an altarpiece for Stavreby church near Præstø. Inscribed: »Thorvald«. H. 120 cm. W. 153,5 cm. Purchased 1845.

A564 Christ Assigns the Leadership of the Church to Saint Peter

Relief. Plaster cast of the marble version used as an antependium in the chapel at the Villa Poggio Imperiale, Florence. The original plaster model A565, Rome 1818. H. 64,5 cm. W. 181 cm.

A565 Christ Assigns the Leadership of the Church to Saint Peter

Relief. Original plaster model. Rome 1818. H. 62,5 cm. W. 179,5 cm. A marble version used as an antependium in the chapel at the Villa Poggio Imperiale, Florence.

A566 Christ Blessing the Children

Relief. Plaster cast. The original plaster model, Nysøe 1839. H. 43,5 cm. W. 74,5 cm.

A567 Jesus as a Child in the Temple

Relief. Original plaster model. Inscribed: »Nysøe d. 8 Marts 1841«. H. 84 cm. W. 72 cm.

A568 Christ and the Woman of Samaria at the Well

Relief. Original plaster model. Inscribed: »Nysøe d. 10 Februar 1841«. H. 77,5 cm. W. 70 cm.

A569 The Annunciation

Relief. Original plaster model. Inscribed: »Roma 20 Marzo 1842«. H. 65,5 cm. W. 125 cm.

A570 The Adoration of the Shepherds

Relief. Original plaster model. Inscribed: »Rom 1. Januar 1842«. H. 65 cm. W. 123 cm.

A571 The Flight into Egypt

Relief. Original plaster model. Rome 1842. H. 68,7 cm. W. 122,5 cm.

A572 Jesus as a Child in the Temple

Relief. Original plaster model. Inscribed: »Roma Maggio 1842«. H. 66,5 cm. W. 123 cm.

A573 The Baptism of Christ

Relief. Original plaster model. Inscribed: »agusto 184(2)«. Rome 1842. H. 66 cm. W. 125 cm.

A574 Christ's Entry into Jerusalem

Relief. Original plaster model. Rome 1842. H. 65,5 cm. W. 94,5 cm.

A575 Matthew

Relief. Marble version of A579 (Rome 1833), executed in Thorvaldsen's studio in Rome between 1833 and 1835. D. 53,2 cm.

A576 Mark

Relief. Marble version of A580 (Rome 1833), executed in 1834 in Thorvaldsen's studio in Rome. D. 53,5 cm.

A577 Luke

Relief. Marble version of A581 (Rome 1833), executed 1834 in Thorvaldsen's studio in Rome. D. 53 cm.

A578 John

Relief. Marble version of A582 (Rome 1833), executed between 1833 and 1835, in Thorvaldsen's studio in Rome. D. 53 cm.

A579 Matthew

Relief. Original plaster model. Rome 1833. D. 53 cm. Marble version, see A575.

A580 Mark

Relief. Original plaster model. Rome 1833. D. 53 cm. Marble version, see A576.

A581 Luke

Relief. Design for a medal for the Accademia di San Luca. Original plaster model. Rome 1833. D. 53 cm. Marble version, see A577.

A582 John

Relief. Original plaster model. Rome 1833. D. 53 cm. Marble version, see A578.

A583 St. Luke Writing his Gospel

Relief. Original plaster model. D. 50,5 cm.

A584 St. Luke as the First Christian Painter

Relief. Original plaster model. D. 53 cm.

A585 Angels Singing

Relief. Marble version of A586 (Rome 1833). H. 38 cm. W. 42,5 cm.

A586 Angels Singing

Relief. Original plaster model. Rome 1833. H. 36,5 cm. W. 40 cm. Marble version, see A585.

A587 Angels Playing

Relief. Marble version of A588 (Rome 1833). H. 39,2 cm. W. 43 cm.

A588 Angels Playing

Relief. Original plaster model. Rome 1833. H. 37 cm. W. 40 cm. Marble version, see A587.

A589 Christmas Joy in Heaven

Relief. Plaster cast. The original plaster model, Nysø 1842. D. 101 cm. Marble version, see A855.

A590 Hovering Angels with Flowers and Garlands

Relief. Original plaster model. Rome 1833. H. 35,5 cm. W. 64,5 cm. A bronze cast on the High Altar of the Novara Cathedral.

A591 Hovering Angels with Flowers and Garlands

Relief. Original plaster model. Rome 1833. H. 38,5 cm. W. 62,5 cm. A bronze cast on the High Altar of the Novara Cathedral.

A592 Three Cupids with a Garland

Relief. Original plaster model. (Copenhagen 1820?). H. 25,5 cm. W. 77 cm. A marble version on the chimney-piece A735.

A593 Angel of the Last Judgement

Relief. Original plaster model. Rome 1842. H. 98 cm. W. 67 cm. See also A908.

A594 Angel of the Last Judgement

Relief. Original plaster model. Rome 1842. H. 79 cm. W. 48 cm.

A595 Angel of the Last Judgement

Relief. Original plaster model. Rome 1842. H. 79,5 cm. W. 48 cm.

A596 The Child's Guardian Angel

Relief. Original plaster model. Copenhagen 1838. H. 69,3 cm. W. 49,5 cm. See also A907. A marble version on the school collection box in the Church of our Lady, Copenhagen.

A597 Christian Charity

Relief. Marble version of A598 (Rome 1810). H. 70 cm. W. 47 cm.

A598 Christian Charity

Relief. Original plaster model. Rome 1810. H. 67,5 cm. W. 48 cm. Marble versions A597 and on the alms box in the Church of Our Lady, Copenhagen.

A599 Christian Charity United with Faith and Hope

Relief. Original plaster model. Rome 1836. H. 45,5 cm. W. 85 cm.

A600 Minerva Protecting Virtue and Revealing Vice

Relief. Original plaster model. Rome 1818. H. 76 cm. W. 60,7 cm. A bronze cast on the base of the Maitland monument on Zakynthos (see A258).

A601 The Graces Listening to Cupid's Song

Relief. Marble version executed in 1836 by J. Scholl in Thorvaldsen's studio in Rome. The original plaster model, Rome 1821. H. 125,5 cm. W. 101,5 cm. See also A602 and A629.

A602 The Graces Listening to Cupid's Song

Relief. Plaster cast, probably of the original plaster model executed 1821 in Rome. H. 124,5 cm. W. 101 cm. Marble versions A602 and on the Andrea Appiani monument in the Palazzo di Brera, Milan. See also A629.

A603 Hans Madsen, Priest of Svanninge, tells Johan Rantzau of the Enemy's Plans

Relief. Original plaster model. Inscribed: »Nysøe den 5 Marts 1841«. H. 137,5 cm. W. 99 cm. A bronze cast in Svanninge church, Funen.

A604 Genius of the Abolition of Villeinage

Relief. Original plaster model. Inscribed: »Kjøbenhavn 12 Debr. 1842«. H. 59 cm. W. 41 cm. See also A809. Executed in marble by C. F. Holbech in Thorvaldsen's studio in Rome and placed on the monument to Frederik VI near Skanderborg in 1845.

A605 Genius of the Establishment of Provincial Consultative Chambers

Relief. Original plaster model. Copenhagen 1842-43. H. 59 cm. W. 41 cm. Executed in marble by C. F. Holbech in Thorvaldsen's studio in Rome and placed on the monument to Frederik VI near Skanderborg in 1845.

A606 Genius of the Rule of Justice

Relief. Original plaster model. Copenhagen 1841-43. H. 59 cm. W. 41 cm. Executed in marble by C. F. Holbech in Thorvaldsen's studio in Rome and placed on the monument to Frederik VI near Skanderborg in 1845.

A607 Genius of the Protection of the Arts and Sciences

Relief. Original plaster model. Inscribed: »Kjøbenhavn den 6 Marts 1843«. H. 59 cm. W. 41 cm. Executed in marble by C. F. Holbech in Thorvaldsen's studio in Rome and placed on the monument to Frederik VI near Skanderborg in 1845.

A608 Genius of the Abolition of Villeinage

Relief, preliminary work for A604. Plaster cast. The original plaster model, Copenhagen 1842. H. 62 cm. W. 44 cm.

A609 Personifications of Justice and Strength

Relief. Preliminary work for A606. Original plaster model. Inscribed: »Kjøbenhavn d:9 Januar 1843«. H. 59 cm. W. 41,5 cm.

A610 Genii Strewing Flowers on the Symbols of the Arts and Sciences

Relief. Preliminary work for A607. Original plaster model. Inscribed: »Kjøbenhavn den 15. Januar 1843«. H. 59,5 cm. W. 42 cm.

A611 Raphael between the Genius of Light and the Goddess of Victory

Relief. Original plaster model. Rome 1833. H. 91,5 cm. W. 129 cm. Intended for Raphael's tomb in the Pantheon in Rome, but not used.

A612 Cardinal Consalvi Restores the Papal Provinces to Pius VII

Relief. Original plaster model. Rome 1825. H. 58 cm. W. 120,7 cm. A marble version on Consalvi's tomb in the Pantheon in Rome. See also A271.

A613 Tobias Heals his Blind Father

Relief. Original plaster model. Rome 1828. H. 103 cm. W. 197 cm.

A marble version on the tomb of the Italian oculist Vacca Berlinghieri (1771-1826) in Campo Santo, Pisa.

A614 Tomb for Auguste Böhmer

Three reliefs. Original plaster models. Rome 1811-12.
1. The Departed Tends her Sick Mother. H. 79 cm. W. 61 cm.
2. Nemesis. H. 78,5 cm. W. 47 cm.
3. The Genius of Death. H. 79 cm. W. 45,5 cm.
The Marble versions A700-702 and the bust A703 were intended for the tomb of August Böhmer (1785-1800) in Bocklet, but never placed.

A615 Tomb for Philipp Bethmann-Hollweg

Three reliefs. Original plaster models. Rome 1814.
1. The Deceased's Brother Bringing him the Emperor of Austria's Reward. H. 90 cm. W. 140 cm.
2. The Sorrowing Mother and Sister of the Deceased. H. 89,5 cm. W. 93,5 cm.
3. Nemesis Recording his Deed and the God of the River Arno. H. 90 cm. W. 97,5 cm.
See also A734. Marble versions formerly on the tomb of Philipp Bethmann-Hollweg (1791-1812), now in the Liebighaus in Frankfurt-on-Main.

A616 Brother and Sister Leaving their Mother on Earth

Relief. Original plaster model. Rome 1835. H. 96,5 cm. W. 155,5 cm. A marble version executed for the tomb of the children of Princess

Helena Poninska in the Palace Chapel in Czerwonogród. Now in the State Museum of Lvov.

A617 Brother and Sister Leaving their Mother on Earth

Relief. Preliminary work for A616. Original plaster model. Rome 1834. H. 38,5 cm. W. 59 cm.

A618 Baron Schubart Bids Farewell to his Wife on her Deathbed

Relief. Original plaster model. Rome 1814. H. 59 cm. W. 90,7 cm. A marble version A704 was executed for the tomb of Baroness Jacoba Elisabeth Schubart, but never placed.

A619 Count Luigi Porro Lambertenghi and his Children Sorrowing

Relief. Original plaster model. Rome 1817. H. 89,5 cm. W. 91,5 cm. Executed in marble for the tomb of Countess Anna Maria Porro Serbelloni together with reliefs representing Nemesis and the Genius of Death, now in the Galleria d'Arte Moderna, Milan.

A620 Man and Wife Reunited in Heaven

Relief. Original plaster model. Rome, c. 1828-30. H. 63,5 cm. W. 56,7 cm. Executed in marble for the tomb of Sir Charles Drake Garrard and wife in the parish church of Wheathampstead, Hertfordshire, England.

A621 Mother Led away from her Son by the Genius of Death

Relief. Original plaster model. Rome 1816. H. 77,2 cm. W. 101 cm. Executed in marble for the tomb of Countess Jozefa Borkowska in the Dominican Church in Lvov.

A622 The Genius of Death and a Woman Kneeling at a Tombstone

Relief. Plaster cast. The original plaster model A740, Rome 1818. H. 74,5 cm. W. 77 cm. Executed in marble for the tomb of Anthony Radcliffe, Earl of Newburgh, in St. Richard's Church, Slindon, Sussex, England.

A623 Woman Kneeling between Two Angels

Relief. Original plaster model. Rome 1828. H. 95 cm. W. 128,5 cm. Executed in marble for the tomb of Lady Jane Lawly in the church of Escrick, Yorkshire, England.

A624 Woman Ascending to Heaven, above the Genius of Death

Relief. Original plaster model. Rome 1818. H. 122,5 cm. W. 96 cm. Executed in marble for the tomb of Baroness Stanislaus Chaudoir. Present location unknown.

A625 Woman Ascending to Heaven, above the Genius of Death

Relief, probably a variation of A624. Original plaster model. H. 125 cm. W. 100 cm.

A626 The Genius of Death

Relief. Marble version of A627 (Rome 1829). H. 88 cm. W. 77 cm.

A627 The Genius of Death

Relief. Original plaster model. Rome 1829. H. 87 cm. W. 73,5 cm. Marble versions A626 and on the tomb of Count Wlodzimierz Potocki (see A155) in the Cathedral on the Wawel in Cracow.

A628 Children Praying

Relief. Original plaster model. Rome 1834. H. 33 cm. W. 47 cm. Marble version on the tomb of count Arthur Potocki in the cathedral on the Wawel in Cracow.

A629 Andrea Appiani

1754–1817. Italian painter. Portrait medallion, executed after a relief by Gaëtano Monti. Original plaster model. Rome c. 1822. D. 46 cm. A marble version of the medallion placed on the Appiani monument in the Palazzo di Brera, Milan (see A602).

A630 Ernst Heinrich Løffler

1723–1796. Danish painter and drawing-master at the Royal Academy of Fine Arts, Copenhagen. Portrait medallion. Plaster cast. The original plaster model A864, Copenhagen 1796. D. 46 cm.

A631 Carlo Bassi

1771–1840. Italian architect. From 1783 settled in Sweden and Finland. Portrait medallion. Plaster cast. The original plaster model, Rome 1797, D. 46,3 cm.

A632 Julius August Walther von Goethe

1789–1830. German. Son of Johann Wolfgang von Goethe. Portrait medallion. Original plaster model. Rome 1831. D. 46 cm. Formerly in marble, now in bronze on the tomb of August von Goethe in the Protestant Cemetery in Rome.

A633 Henrich Steffens

1773–1845. Danish philosopher and naturalist. Portrait medallion. Original plaster model. Nysø 1840. D. 46 cm.

A634 Heinrich Reinhold

1788–1825. German painter. Portrait medallion. Original plaster model. Rome 1825. D. 46,5 cm. Formerly in marble, now in bronze on the tomb of Reinhold in the Protestant Cemetery in Rome.

A635 Christina Alexandra Egypta Bonaparte?

1798–1847. Daughter of Lucien Bonaparte. Portrait medallion. Original plaster model. Rome, probably 1818. D. 46,3 cm. Marble version, see A726.

A636 Thorvaldsen with the Stampe Family

From left to right: Christian Stampe, Thorvaldsen, Jeanina, Bar-

oness Christine, and Elise Stampe. On the modelling stand a bozzetto for the statue of the apostle Andrew (see A108).
Relief. Plaster cast. Inscribed: »Nysøe d. 5 Oct 1840«. H. 60,3 cm. W. 99,5 cm.

A637 Baron Stampe and his Sons

From left to right: Holger, Henrik and Baron Henrik Stampe. Relief. Plaster cast. The original plaster model, Nysø 1840. H. 60,3 cm. W. 99,8 cm.

A638-A641

A series of reliefs representing the Ages of Man and the Seasons. Reliefs. Marble versions of A642-A645 (Rome 1836). D. 69 cm.

A638 Childhood – Spring

See above.

A639 Youth – Summer

See above.

A640 Manhood – Autumn

See above.

A641 Old Age – Winter

See above.

A642-A645

A series of reliefs representing the Ages of Man and the Seasons. Reliefs. Original plaster models. Rome 1836. D. 67,5 cm. Marble versions, see A638-A641.

A642 Childhood – Spring

See above.

A643 Youth – Summer

See above.

A644 Manhood – Autumn

See above.

A645 Old Age – Winter

Se above.

A646 Hunter on a Horse

Relief. Original plaster model. Rome 1834. H. 105 cm. W. 113,5 cm. Marble version, see A792.

A647 Huntress on a Horse

Relief. Original plaster model. Rome 1834. H. 105,5 cm. W. 123 cm. Marble version, see A793.

A648 Bacchante with a Bird

Relief. Original plaster model. Rome 1837. H. 49,8 cm. W. 44,3 cm.

A700 Nemesis

Tomb for Auguste Böhmer: A700-03.
Relief. Marble version (Thorvaldsen) of A614 completed in 1814. H. 77,6 cm. W. 45,7 cm.

A701 The Departed Tends her Sick Mother

Tomb for Auguste Böhmer: A700-03.
Relief. Marble version (Thorvaldsen) of A614 completed 1814. H. 77,5 cm. W. 63 cm.

A702 The Genius of Death

Tomb for Auguste Böhmer: A700-03.
Relief. Marble version (Thorvaldsen) of A614 completed 1814. H. 77,5 cm. W. 45 cm.

A703 Auguste Böhmer

1785-1800. Daughter of the German physician J. F. N. Böhmer.
Bust. Marble version (Thorvaldsen) executed 1811-1814 after a bust by Chr. Fr. Tieck (G245) intended for the monument for which Thorvaldsen executed the reliefs A700-02. H. 39 cm.

A704 Baron Herman Schubart Bids Farewell to his Wife on her Deathbed

Relief. Tomb for Baroness Jacoba Elisabeth Schubart. Marble version (Thorvaldsen) of A618 (Rome 1814). H. 58,9 cm. W. 93,5 cm.

A705 The Dance of the Muses on Helicon

Apollo, the Muses, and the Graces. Relief. Unifinished. Marble version (Thorvaldsen) of the original plaster model executed in 1804 at Montenero. H. 73 cm. W. 160 cm. See also A340-41.

A706 Stanislaw Kossakowski

1795-1872. Polish count.
Bust. Marble version (Thorvaldsen) of A295 (Rome 1825). H. 57,5 cm.

A707 Griffin and Lyre

Relief, fragment. Probably an original plaster model. Rome c. 1835. H. 64 cm. W. 67,2 cm. Modelled for the base of the Schiller monument (see A135-37 and A770).

A708 Lyre

Relief, fragment. Probably an original plaster model. Rome c. 1835. H. 57,2 cm. W. 35 cm. Modelled for the base of the Schillermonument (see A135-37 and A770).

A709 Base for the Gutenberg Monument with the Relief »The Invention of the Movable Type«.

Sketch model. Plaster. Rome c. 1833-34. H. 32. W. 46,9 to 48,5 cm. See A114-15.

A710 Victory Writing on a Shield

Relief. Reworked plaster cast of A361. Rome c. 1830. H. 92,5 cm. W. 71,5 cm.

A711 Coronation Medal with Crown, Sceptre, and Sword

Design for the reverse of a medal on the occasion of the coronation of Christian VIII.
Probably an original plaster model. Copenhagen c. 1840. D. 32,2 cm. Attributed to Thorvaldsen.

A712 Alexander the Great in his Triumphal Chariot

Relief. Variation of the central section of A508. Original plaster model. H. 57 cm. W. 101 cm. Marble version, see A509.

A713 Alexander the Great in his Triumphal Chariot

Relief, fragment. Probably an original plaster model for the central section of the Alexander Frieze for Christiansborg Palace. H. 115 cm. W. 105 cm. to 81 cm.

A714 Two Men on Horse-back in the Train of Alexander the Great

Relief. Section of a recast of A505. Plaster cast. The original plaster model probably executed in Rome 1812. H. 109 cm. W. 152,5 cm. to 164 cm.

A715 Alexander I

1777-1825. Czar of Russia 1801. Bust. Original plaster model. Warsaw 1820. H. 52 cm. Marble version, see A883. See also A246.

A716 Caroline Amalie

1796-1881. Princess, later Queen of Denmark, married to Christian Frederik (Christian VIII) Bust. Original plaster model. Rome 1820-21. H. 39 cm. See also A198 and A754.

A717 George Gordon, Lord Byron

1788-1824, English poet. Bust. Plaster cast; the head of A256. Rome c. 1817. H. 55 cm.

A718 Herman Schubart

1756-1832. Danish baron and diplomat in Italy (Leghorn). Bust. Original plaster model. Montenero 1804. H. 72 cm. Marble version, see A219. See also A812.

A719 Jacoba Elisabeth Schubart

1765-1814. Née de Wieling, married to Baron Herman Schubart. Bust. Original plaster model. Montenero 1804. H. 58,7 cm. Marble version, see A220. See also A813.

A720 Wilhelmine Benigna Biron

1781-1839. Duchess of Sagan. Bust. Plaster cast before the addition of curls on the forehead and temples. The original plaster model A312, Rome 1818. H. 58,5 cm. See also A811.

A721 François Gabriel de Bray

1765-1832. French by birth, entered Bavarian service as a diplomat. Bavarian Count. Bust. Plaster cast. Inscribed: »A«. The original plaster model A300, Rome c. 1818-19. H. 51,5 cm.

A722 Leonardo Pisano, Fibonacci

C. 1170-c. 1240. Italian mathematician. Bust. Original plaster model. Rome between 1834 and 1838. H. 73 cm. Marble version, see A187.

A723 Head of a Woman with Tiara

Head executed for the restoration of an antique bronze statue in the Glyptothek, Munich, the so-called »Spinnerin«. Original plaster model. Rome 1837. H. 37,5 cm.

A724 Andreas Peter Bernstorff

1735-1797. Danish statesman and count. Mask. Plaster cast of A856. Inscribed: »A. P. Bernstorff afst. af buste«. The original plaster model, Copenhagen 1795. H. 23,6 cm.

A725 Karl Philipp von Schwarzenberg

1771-1820. Austrian prince and general, Duke of Krumau.
Mask. Plaster cast, probably of an earlier version of the bust A236. Rome 1821. H. 26 cm.

A726 Christina Alexandra Egypta Bonaparte?

1798-1847. Daughter of Lucien Bonaparte.
Portrait medallion. Marble version of A635 (Rome, probably 1818). D. 49 cm.

A727 Marianna Florenzi

1802-1870. Née Baccinetti, married to Marchese Ettore Florenzi.
Bust. Marble version of A278 (Rome 1828), begun by Thorvaldsen in 1829 in Rome, and completed in 1858 in Copenhagen under the supervision of H. W. Bissen. H. 74,4 cm.

A728 Pan and Hunting Nymph

Relief. Marble version of A356 (Rome c. 1838). H. 69,7 cm. W. 60,7 cm.

A729 Cupid and the Tamed Lion

Relief. Marble version of A387 (Rome 1828). H. 49 cm. W. 65,5 cm.

A730 The Baptism of Christ

Relief. Plaster cast. The original plaster model, Copenhagen 1820. H. 95 cm. W. 223,5 cm. See also A557.

A731 Hymen

Relief. Probably an original plaster model. D. 94 cm.

A732 Napoleon I

1769-1821. Emperor of France 1804-14.
Bust. Marble version of A909 (Rome c. 1830), begun in Rome and completed in Copenhagen under the supervision of H. W. Bissen. H. 99,9 cm. See also A252 and A867.

A733 Ganymede with Jupiter's Eagle

Statue. Plaster cast of a reduced version of A44. H. 37 cm. to 46,5 cm. W. 59,5 cm.

A734 Woman Sorrowing

Relief, fragment from the tomb of Philipp Bethmann-Hollweg. Plaster cast. The original plaster model, Rome 1814. H. 88,5 cm. W. 33 cm to 29 cm. See also A615.

A735 Chimney-Piece with Two Caryatids and a Frieze of Cupids.

Relief. Marble. Rome, early 1820(?). H. 135,5 cm. W. 201,5 cm. See A56 and A592.

A736 The Baptism of Christ

Relief. Probably an original plaster model executed for the Brahetrolleborg Baptismal Font (1805-07). H. 82 cm. W. 54 cm. to 63 cm. See A555.

A737 Christ Blessing the Children

Relief. Probably an original plaster model executed for the Brahetrolleborg Baptismal Font (1805-07). H. 71 cm. W. 54 cm. See A555.

A738 Thorvaldsen, Sommariva and a Greek Warrior

Relief. Original plaster model. Rome c. 1825. H. 103 cm. W. 136 cm. to 129 cm. The end-piece of the Alexander Frieze executed for Count G. B. Sommariva. See A505.

A739 The Ages of Love

Relief. An adaptation of A427. Probably an original plaster model. Copenhagen 1843. H. 50,5 cm. W. 144 cm. See also A426.

A740 The Genius of Death and a Woman Kneeling at a Tombstone

Relief. Original plaster model. Rome 1818. H. 76 cm. W. 81 cm. Executed in marble for the tomb of Anthony Radcliffe, Earl of Newburgh, in St. Richard's Church, Slindon, Sussex, England. See also A622.

A741 Giovanni-Battista Sommariva

C. 1750-1826. Italian count, politician, and art collector. Bust. Marble version of A273 (Rome 1817 or 1818). H. 51,7 cm. See also A272.

A742 Perseus on Pegasus Rescuing Andromeda

Relief. Original plaster model. Nysø 1839. D. 77 cm.

A743 Andreas Peter Bernstorff

1735-1797. Danish statesman and count. Portrait medallion. Plaster cast. Inscribed: »B. Thorvaldsen F. 1796«. The original plaster model A817, Copenhagen 1796. D. 35,7 cm.

A744 Peter Johan Monrad

1758-1834. Danish high-ranking civil servant. Portrait medallion. Probably a plaster cast, painted. Copenhagen before 1796. D. 42 cm.

A745 Cecilia Kirstine Monrad

1761-1839. Married to Peter Johan Monrad. Portrait medallion. Probably a plaster cast, painted. Copenhagen, before 1796. D. 41,5 cm.

A746 Peter Johan Monrad.

1758-1834. Danish high-ranking civil servant. Portrait medallion. Probably a plaster cast, painted. Copenhagen before 1796. D. 42 cm.

A747 Cecilia Kirstine Monrad

1761-1839. Married to Peter Johan Monrad. Portrait medallion. Probably a plaster cast, painted. Copenhagen before 1796. D. 42 cm.

A748 King Numa Pompilius Conversing with the Nymph Egeria in her Grotto

Relief. Plaster cast. Inscribed: »B. Thorvaldsen: Fec. 1794«. Copenhagen. H. 48 cm. W. 61 cm.

A749 Hercules and Omphale

Relief. Plaster cast. Copenhagen 1792. H. 48 cm. W. 60 cm.

A750 Mother and Two Children

Statuette. Original plaster model. Copenhagen c. 1793. H. 38,5 cm. Purchased in 1850 at an auction over the estate of the widow of the Danish painter N. A. Abildgaard.

A751 Homer

7th century B. C. Greek poet.
Bust. Marble version (Thorvaldsen). Rome 1799. Copy of an antique bust. H. 51,4 cm. Purchased 1850 at an auction over the estate of the widow of the Danish painter N. A. Abildgaard.

A752 Raphael

1483-1520. Italian artist.
Bust. Marble version (Thorvaldsen). Rome 1800. Copy of a bust of Raphael by Pietro Paolo Naldini, placed 1674 in the Pantheon in Rome and moved in 1820 to La Protomoteca on the Capitoline Hill. H. 54 cm. Purchased in 1850 at an auction over the estate of the widow of the Danish painter N. A. Abildgaard.

A753 Christian Frederik

1786-1848. Danish prince, from 1839 King Christian VIII of Denmark.
Bust. Original plaster model. Rome 1821. H. 69 cm. See also A197.

A754 Caroline Amalie

1796-1881. Princess, later Queen of Danmark, married to Christian Frederik (Christian VIII).
Bust. Plaster cast. The original plaster model A716, Rome 1820-21. H. 67 cm. See also A198.

A755 Shepherd Boy

Sketch model for A177. Plaster. Rome 1817. H. 52,5 cm. Purchased 1854 from the Buti family in Rome. Thorvaldsen lived in the Casa Buti in the Via Sistina.

A756 Cupid Resting

Oval relief. Original plaster model. Inscribed: »Thorvaldsen fec.« Copenhagen 1789. H. 76,5 cm. W. 56 cm. Awarded the Major Silver Medal of the Academy of Fine Arts, Copenhagen. Presented by the Academy in 1855.

A757 The Muse Euterpe

Statuette. Original plaster model, painted. Copenhagen 1794. H. 49,2 cm. Sketch model for a statue in Prince Frederik's (later Christian X's) palace at Amalienborg, from a composition by N. A. Abildgaard. Presented by the Academy of Fine Arts in 1855.

A758 The Muse Terpsichore

Statuette. Original plaster model, painted. Copenhagen 1794. H. 49,5 cm. Sketch model for a statue in Prince Frederik's (later Christian X's) palace at Amalienborg, from a composition by N. A. Abildgaard. Presented by the Academy of Fine Arts 1855.

A759 Agrippa

63 B. C. – 12 B. C. Roman consul and commander.

Bust. Marble version (Thorvaldsen). Rome 1799-1800. Copy of an antique bust. H. 50,5 cm. Presented by the Academy of Fine Arts in 1855.

A760 Cicero

106 B. C. – 43 B. C. Roman statesman and orator

Bust. Marble version (Thorvaldsen). Rome 1799-1800. Copy of an antique bust. H. 43 cm. Presented by the Academy of Fine Arts in 1855.

A761 Cicero

106 B. C. – 43 B. C. Roman statesman and orator.

Bust. Marble version (Thorvaldsen). Rome 1799-1800. Copy of an antique bust. H. 48,5 cm. Presented by the Academy of Fine Arts in 1855.

A762 Maximilian I

See A128

A763 Sophie Dorothea Høyer

C. 1743-1808. Née Heldvad, married to Pastor Jens Offesen Høyer. The mother of the painter Christian Fædder Høyer.

Bust. Marble version (Thorvaldsen) of A228 (Rome 1809). H. 39,6 cm. Bequeathed by C. F. Høyer in 1855.

A764 Simon Jensen

1749-1800. Danish bookkeeper, administrator of The Danish West India Trading Company.

Portrait medallion. Original plaster model, painted. Inscribed: »B. Thorvaldsen Fec 1793«. Copenhagen. D. 42 cm. Presented by C. J. Glahn in 1856.

A765 Eleonora Maria Jensen

Née Weygaard, married to Simon Jensen.

Portrait medallion. Original plaster model, painted. Inscribed: »B. Thorvaldsen Fec 1793«. Copenhagen. D. 42 cm. Presented by C. J. Glahn in 1856.

A766 The Children of Simon Jensen

Left: Anna Birgitte Margrethe (1784-1823), later married to pharmacist Hans Egede Glahn. Right: Johan Otto Jensen (1786-1809).

Portrait medallion. Original plaster model, painted. Inscribed: »B. Thorvaldsen Fec 1793«. Copenhagen. D. 41 cm. Presented by C. J. Glahn, in 1856.

A767 Simon Jensen

1749-1800. Danish bookkeeper, administrator of The Danish West India Trading Company.

Portrait medallion. Plaster cast of the original plaster model A764, Copenhagen 1793. D. 42 cm.

A768 Eleonora Maria Jensen

Née Weygaard, married to Simon Jensen.

Portrait medallion. Plaster cast of the original plaster model A765, Copenhagen 1793. D. 42 cm.

A769 The Children of Simon Jensen

Left: Anna Birgitte Margrethe (1784-1823), later married to pharmacist Hans Egede Glahn. Right:

Johan Otto Jensen (1786-1809). Portrait medallion. Plaster cast of the original plaster model A766, Copenhagen 1793. D. 41 cm.

A770 Friedrich Schiller

1759-1805. German poet. Statue. Original plaster model. Rome 1836. H. 391 cm. Modelled by W. Matthiä after Thorvaldsen's sketch model (see A138). Erected in bronze in Stuttgart in 1839. Purchased in 1857 fom the Württembergische Kunstschule, Stuttgart.

A771 Bertel Thorvaldsen Leaning on the Statue of Hope

1770-1844. Self-portrait. Statue. Marble version executed in 1859 for the Museum by H. W. Bissen. The original plaster model, Nysø 1839. H. 198 cm. See also A162.

A772 The Hours

Relief. Plaster cast. The original plaster model Dep. 22 executed in 1794 in Copenhagen for Prince Frederik's (later Christian X's) palace at Amalienborg, from a composition by N. A. Abildgaard. H. 57 cm. W. 94 cm. Presented by the restorer P. H. Rasmussen in 1865.

A773 Georgiana Elizabeth Russell

C. 1810-1867. Daughter of John Russell, Duke of Bedford. Statue. Marble version of A173 executed in 1866 by Christian Freund under the supervision of H. W. Bissen. The original plaster model, Rome 1815. H. 101,2 cm.

A774 Hector with Paris and Helen

Relief. Marble version of A499 (Rome 1809) executed 1868 for the Museum by Christian Freund under the supervision of H. W. Bissen. H. 72 cm. W. 94 cm.

A775 Priam Pleads with Achilles for Hector's Body

Relief. Marble version of A492 (Rome 1815) executed in 1868-70 for the Museum by Christian Freund under the supervivision of H. W. Bissen. H. 96 cm. W. 198,5 cm.

A776 Hector's Farewell to Andromache

Relief. Marble version of A501 (Rome 1837) executed in 1867-70 by H. W. and V. Bissen. H. 93,5 cm. W. 184,2 cm. Presented by the brewer J. C. Jacobsen in 1870.

A777 Achilles and Penthesilea

Statuette. Original plaster model. Rome 1801. H. 65,5 cm. Bequeathed by J. M. Thiele in 1875.

A778 Dancing Girl

Sketch model for A178. Plaster. Rome, probably 1817. H. 54,5 cm. Purchased 1875.

A779 Actaeon Torn by his Dogs

Oval relief. Plaster cast. H. 33,5 cm. W. 25 cm. See A461. Presented by the sculptor C. Freund in 1875.

A780 Cupid Stung by a Bee Complains to Venus

Relief. Original plaster model.
Rome 1809. H. 46 cm. W. 51,5 cm.
Marble version, see A417. Presented by the sculptor C. Freund in 1876.

A781 Angel Kneeling with a Baptismal Font

Bozzetto for A112. Terracotta.
Rome, probably 1823. H. 30,7 cm.
Bequeathed by Consul Johan Bravo 1876.

A782 Bernt Anker?

1746-1805. Norwegian owner of ironworks.
Portrait medallion. Terracotta.
Copenhagen c. 1796. D. 21,5 cm.
Purchased 1879.

A783 Minerva

Bozzetto. Terracotta. Fragment of the clay model for A17 (Copenhagen 1843). H. 7,7 cm. W. 5,5 cm.
Purchased 1879.

A784 Aesculapius

Bozzetto. Terracotta. Fragment of the clay model for A20 (Copenhagen 1843). H. 10,5 cm. W. 6,3 cm.
Purchased 1879.

A785 Genius

Bozzetto. Terracotta. Fragment of the clay model for A607. Inscribed: »6 Mai 1843«. Copenhagen. H. 7 cm. W. 5,5 cm. Purchased 1879.

A786 Cupid Playing a Lyre

Statue. Original plaster model.
Rome 1819. H. 60 cm. Marble version, see A33. Purchased 1882.

A787 The Royal Coat of Arms

Relief. Painted sandstone.
Copenhagen 1789. H. 70 cm.
W. 205 cm. Executed for the Court Pharmacy, formerly at 25 Store Kongensgade, Copenhagen. Presented by Mr. Ibsen, Court Pharmacist, in 1882.

A788 Christoffer Wilhelm Eckersberg

1783-1853. Danish painter.
Bust. Marble version (Thorvaldsen) of A224 (Rome 1816). Inscribed:
»ECKERSBERG PITTORE/THORVALDSEN · FACEVA ROMA · LI · XII · MAGGIO · MDCCCXVI«. H. 53,5 cm. Presented by C. W. Eckersberg's daughters in 1883.

A789 Adonis

Statue. Plaster cast of the marble version in Munich. The original plaster model A53, Rome 1808.
H. 185 cm. Purchased 1886.

A790 Adonis

Statue. Marble version of A53 (Rome 1808) and A789 executed in 1887 for the Museum by A. Saabye. H. 186 cm.

A791 Achilles and Priam

Relief. Original plaster model.
Copenhagen 1791. H. 67 cm.
W. 78,5 cm. Presented by the Academy of Fine Arts in 1887.

A792 Hunter on a Horse

Relief. Marble version of A646 (Rome 1834) executed in 1886-87 for the Museum by C. Aarsleff under the supervision of C. Peters.
H. 103 cm. W. 114 cm.

A793 Huntress on a Horse

Relief. Marble version of A647 (Rome 1834) executed in 1886-87 for the Museum by C. Aarsleff under the supervision of C. Peters. H. 102 cm. W. 123,3 cm.

A794 Wlodzimierz Potocki

1789-1812. Polish count and general.
Statue. Marble version of A155 (Rome 1821) executed in 1886-88 for the Museum by V. Bissen. H. 215,3 cm.

A795 Jon Erichsen

1728-1787. Born in Iceland, lawyer and philologist.
Mask. Plaster. H. 20 cm. Probably a cast of a fragment of the Erichsen bust which was executed in plaster in Copenhagen in 1794 and broke during its transportation from Copenhagen to Iceland in 1825. See also A862. Purchased 1888.

A796 Mercury Brings the Infant Bacchus to Ino

Relief. Marble version of A347 (Rome 1809) executed in 1889 for the Museum by R. Andersen under the supervision of T. Stein. H. 48,5 cm. W. 49 cm.

A797 Cupid and Bacchus

Relief. Marble version of the original plaster model (Rome 1810?) in the Museum of Fine Arts in Randers executed in 1889 for the Museum by R. Andersen under the supervision of T. Stein. H.53 cm. W. 72,3 cm.

A798 The Centaur Chiron Teaching Achilles to Throw a Spear

Relief. Marble version of A488 (Rome 1837) executed in 1888-90 for the Museum by R. Andersen under the supervision of T. Stein. H. 101,5 cm. W. 123,5 cm.

A802 Jacob Baden

1735-1804. Danish author and philologist.
Bust. Original plaster model. Inscribed: »B. Thorvaldsen f.«. Rome 1806. H. 33,3 cm. Formerly believed to represent the Danish archaeologist Georg Zoëga. Marble version, see A803. See also A863. Purchased 1898.

A803 Jacob Baden

1735-1804. Danish author and philologist.
Bust. Marble version of A802 (Rome 1806) executed by T. Stein. Inscribed:»1755 G. Zoëga. 1809« and on the back: »B. Thorvaldsen Rom«. H. 31 cm. See also A863. Purchased 1898.

A804 Cupid Triumphant

Statue. Marble version of A22 executed in 1897-99 for the Museum by R. Andersen under the supervision of T. Stein. The original plaster model, Rome 1814. H. 144 cm.

A805 Cupid's Torso

Relief. Terracotta. Fragment of the clay model for A450 (Nysø 1840). Inscribed: »Af A. Thorvaldsens egenhændige Modellering paa Nysø 1841-44.« H. 16,5 cm. Purchased 1900.

A806 Cupid's Head

Relief. Terracotta. Fragment of the clay model for A450 (Nysø 1840). Inscribed: »Af A. Thorvaldsens egenhændige Modellering paa Nysø 1841-44.« H. 7,5 cm. Purchased 1900.

A807 Cupid's Wing

Relief. Terracotta. Fragment of the clay model for A450 (Nysø 1840). Inscribed: »A. Thorvaldsens originale Arbejde paa Nysø 1841-44.« H. 14,5 cm. Purchased 1900.

A808 Psyche's Head

Relief. Terracotta. Fragment of the clay model for A450 (Nysø 1840). Inscribed: »A. Thorvaldsens egenhændige Modellering paa Nysø 1841-44.« H. 10 cm. Purchased 1900.

A809 Fragment of a Leg

Relief. Terracotta. Fragment of the clay model for A604 (Copenhagen 1842). Inscribed: »Af A. Thorvaldsens originale Arbejde paa Nysø 1841-44.« H. 10,3 cm. Purchased 1900.

A810 Ida Brun

1792-1857. Daughter of Constantin and Friederike Brun. Married Count Louis Philippe Bombelles, Austrian diplomat.
Bust. Marble version (Thorvaldsen) of A218 (Rome 1809). H. 56,5 cm. Bequeathed by Fritz Brun, Royal Chamberlain, 1902.

A811 Wilhelmine Benigna Biron

1781-1839. Duchess of Sagan. Bust. Plaster cast before the addition of curls on the forehead and temples. The original plaster model A312, Rome 1818. H. 58 cm. See also A720. Presented in 1909 by Baron August Binzer, Munich.

A812 Herman Schubart

1756-1832. Danish baron and diplomat in Italy (Leghorn). Bust. Plaster cast of A219. The original plaster model A718, Montenero 1804. H. 70,4 cm. Presented by the Academy of Fine Arts in 1910.

A813 Jacoba Elisabeth Schubart

1765-1814. Née de Wieling. Married to Baron Herman Schubart. Bust. Plaster cast of A220. The original plaster model A719, Montenero 1804. H. 70,4 cm. Presented by the Academy of Fine Arts in 1910.

A814 Head of a Bacchante

Relief. Terracotta. Fragment of the clay model for A358 (Nysø 1840-41). Inscribed: »Af A. Thorvaldsens egenhændige Modellering paa Nysø 1841-44«. H. 8 cm. Purchased 1910.

A815 Michael Rosing

1756-1818. Danish actor.
Portrait medallion. Plaster, painted.
Inscribed: »B. Thorvaldsen
fec. 1793«. Copenhagen. D. 42 cm.
Purchased 1910.

A816 Johanne Cathrine Rosing

1756-1853. Danish actress, née
Olsen.
Portrait medallion. Plaster, painted.
Inscribed: »B. Thorvaldsen Fec
(1793?)«. Copenhagen. D. 42 cm.
Purchased 1910.

A817 Andreas Peter Bernstorff

1735-1797. Danish statesman and
count.
Portrait medallion. Original plaster
model, painted and gilded. Inscribed: »B. Thorvaldsen født [sic]
1796«. Copenhagen. D. 42 cm.
Purchased 1911.

A818 Louise Augusta

1771-1843. Danish princess, married to Count Frederik Christian of
Augustenborg.
Portrait medallion. Original plaster
model, painted and gilded. Inscribed: »Thorvaldsen Fec 1793«.
Copenhagen. D. 42 cm. Purchased
1911.

A819 Cupid Standing with his Bow

Statue. Marble version of A36
(Rome, probably 1819). Inscribed:
»Thorvaldsen. F.« H. 101 cm.
Purchased 1914.

A820 Conradin

1252-1268. The last of the Hohen-
staufens.
Sketch model. Plaster cast of A151
(Rome 1833). H. 52 cm. Presented
by the Ny Carlsberg Glyptotek,
Copenhagen, 1915.

A821 Psyche with the Jar of Beauty

Statue. Marble version (Thorvaldsen) of A26 (Rome 1806) H. 132
cm. Purchased at the Hope Auction, »The Deepdene«, Surrey,
England in 1917.

A822 Jason with the Golden Fleece

Statue. Marble version (Thorvaldsen) of A52 (Rome 1802-03). Inscribed: »A«. Commissioned by
Thomas Hope 1803, completed in
1828 in Rome. H. 242 cm. Purchased at the Hope Auction,
»The Deepdene«, Surrey, England
in 1917.

A823 Thomas Hope

1769-1831. English art collector and
author.
Bust. Marble version (Thorvaldsen)
of A298 (Rome 1817). H. 55,4 cm.
Purchased at the Hope Auction,
»The Deepdene«, Surrey, England
in 1917.

A824 Louisa Hope

C. 1786-1851. Née de la Poer Beres-
ford, married to Thomas Hope.
Bust. Marble version (Thorvaldsen)
of A264 (Rome 1817). H. 58,5 cm.
Purchased at the Hope Auction,
»The Deepdene«, Surrey, England
in 1917.

A825 Henry Thomas Hope

1808-1862. Son of Thomas and Louisa Hope.
Bust. Marble version (Thorvaldsen) of A265 (Rome c. 1822-23). H. 47,2 cm. Purchased at the Hope Auction, »The Deepdene«, Surrey, England in 1917.

A826 Adrian John Hope

1811-1863. Son of Thomas and Louisa Hope.
Bust. Marble version (Thorvaldsen) of the original plaster model executed c. 1817 in Rome. H. 41,5 cm. Purchased at the Hope Auction, »The Deepdene«, Surrey, England 1917.

A827 Cupid Received by Anacreon

Relief. Marble version (Thorvaldsen) of the original plaster model executed in 1823 in Rome. From Anacreontea, Song 3, which also inspired H. C. Andersen to write the story of »The Mischievous Boy«. Presented by Thorvaldsen to Thomas Hope in 1828. H. 48,5 cm. W. 70 cm. See also A415. Purchased at the Hope Auction, »The Deepdene«, Surrey, England 1917.

A828 Art and the Light-bringing Genius, *A Genio Lumen*.

Relief. Marble version (Thorvaldsen) of A518 (Rome 1808). Presented by Thorvaldsen to Thomas Hope 1828. H. 99,5 cm. W. 131,5 cm. Purchased at the Hope Auction, »The Deepdene«, Surrey, England 1917.

A829 Heliodorus Driven out of the Temple

Relief. Original plaster model. Copenhagen 1791. Awarded the Minor Gold Medal of the Royal Academy of Fine Arts, Copenhagen. H. 114 cm. W. 173 cm. Presented by the Academy of Fine Arts in 1918.

A830 The Apostles Peter and John Healing a Lame Man before the Gate of the Temple.

Relief. Original plaster model. Copenhagen 1793. Awarded the Major Gold Medal of the Academy of Fine Arts, Copenhagen. H. 117,5 cm. W. 173,5 cm. Presented by the Academy of Fine Arts in 1918.

A831-A850 Fragments of the Alexander Frieze

20 relief fragments from the Alexander Frieze executed for Christiansborg Palace. Marble. Commissioned in 1818 and partly destroyed by fire in 1884. See A503. Presented by the Ministry of Internal Affairs in 1919.

A851 Christian August Tiedge

1752-1841. German poet.
Bust. Marble version (Thorvaldsen) of A240 (Rome c. 1805-06). H. 60,5 cm. Purchased 1920.

A852 Elisabeth (Elisa) von der Recke

1754-1833. German countess and poetess, née von Medem.
Bust. Marble version (Thorvaldsen)

of the original plaster model executed 1805-06 in Rome. H. 69,3 cm. See also A869 and A879. Purchased 1920.

A853 Venus with the Apple Awarded by Paris

Statue. Marble version (Thorvaldsen) of A12 (Rome 1813-16), probably executed for P. C. Labouchére. Inscribed: »Thorwaldsen. F.«. H. 160,8 cm. Purchased 1920.

A854 Ganymede Offering the Cup

Statue. Marble version (Thorvaldsen) of the original plaster model executed in 1804 in Rome. Inscribed: »AT«. H. 136,5 cm. See also A41. Purchased 1920.

A855 Christmas Joy in Heaven

Relief. Marble version (Thorvaldsen), unfinished. The original plaster model, Nysø 1842. D. 101 cm. See also A589. Entered in the inventory in 1921.

A856 Andreas Peter Bernstorff

1735-1797. Danish statesman and count.
Bust. Old plaster cast. Inscribed: »B. Thorvaldsen Fec 179(5).« Copenhagen. H. 80,8 cm. See also A208. Presented by the Ministry of Internal Affairs in 1922.

A857 Caroline

1793-1881. Danish princess, daughter of Frederik VI.
Bust. Marble version (Thorvaldsen) of A193 (Copenhagen 1819-20). Inscribed: »Thorvaldsen F«. H. 69 cm. Purchased 1922.

A858 Nicolaus Copernicus

1473-1543. Astronomer.
Sketch model for A113. Plaster. Rome 1821. H. 46 cm. Presented by shipowner Marius Nielsen in 1922.

A859 Frederik VI

1768-1839. King of Denmark from 1808.
Bust. Marble version (Thorvaldsen) of the original plaster model executed 1819-20 in Copenhagen. Inscribed: »Thorvaldsen F«. H. 69,3 cm. See also A191. Purchased 1923.

A860 Marie Sophie Frederikke

1767-1852. Queen of Denmark, married to Frederik VI.
Bust. Marble version (Thorvaldsen) of A192 (Copenhagen 1819-20). Inscribed: »Thorvaldsen F«. H. 72,8 cm. Purchased 1923.

A861 Karoline von Rehfues

1799-1892. Née von Meusebach, married to the German author Philipp Joseph von Rehfues.
Bust. Marble version (Thorvaldsen) of A245 (Rome 1827). H. 54,7 cm. Purchased 1923.

A862 Jon Erichsen

1728-1787. Born in Iceland, lawyer and philologist.
Mask. Plaster. H. 20 cm. Probably a cast of a fragment of the Erichsen bust which was executed in plaster in Copenhagen in 1794 and broke during its transportation from Copenhagen to Iceland in 1825. See also A795. Purchased 1923.

A863 Jacob Baden

1735-1804. Danish author and philologist.
Bust. Marble version (Thorvaldsen) of the original plaster model executed 1806 in Rome after a death mask and a painted portrait. H. 54,8 cm. See also A802 and A803. Purchased 1924.

A864 Ernst Heinrich Løffler

1723-1796. Danish painter and drawing-master at the Royal Academy of Fine Arts, Copenhagen.
Portrait medallion. Original plaster model. Copenhagen 1796. D. 57 cm. See also A630. Presented by the sculptor E. Utzon-Frank in 1926.

A866 Cupid Revives the Swooning Psyche

Relief. Marble version (Thorvaldsen) of A431 (Montenero 1810). H. 49,5 cm. W. 78 cm. See also A430. Purchased 1926.

A867 Napoleon I

1769-1821. Emperor of France 1804-14.
Bust. Marble version (Thorvaldsen) of A909 (Rome c. 1830). H. 99,9 cm. See also A252 and A732. Purchased 1929.

A868 Mercury about to Kill Argus

Sketch model for A5. Plaster. Rome 1818. H. 52,2 cm. Formerly in the collection of the composer F. Mendelssohn-Bartholdy. Purchased 1931.

A869 Elisabeth (Elisa) von der Recke

1754-1833. German countess and poetess, née von Medem.
Bust. Marble version (Thorvaldsen) of A879 (Rome 1805-06). H. 41,8 cm. See also A852. Purchased 1931.

A870 Hebe

Statue. An adaptation of A37, probably an original plaster model. Rome 1816. H. 155 cm. Marble version, see A874. See also A39. Purchased 1934.

A871 Charlotte Dorothea Fischer

1784-1855. Née Schweffel, married to the Danish officer Frederik Fischer.
Portrait medallion. Plaster cast. The original plaster model, Rome, between 1833 and 1837. D. 31,5 cm. Purchased 1934.

A872 Man on Horseback

Relief. Decoration above a gateway, carved in wood by Thorvaldsen in 1792 in Copenhagen after a drawing by the Navy sculptor F. C. Willerup for 17 Ny Vestergade. H. 123 cm. W. 137,2 cm. Presented by Den sjællandske Bondestands Sparekasse in 1936.

A873 Mercury about to Kill Argus

Statue. Marble version (Thorvaldsen) of A5 (Rome 1818). Inscribed: »A. Thorvaldsen fecit«. H. 174,5 cm. Purchased from Lord Ashburton, »The Grange«, Hampshire in 1938.

A874 Hebe

Statue. Marble version (Thorvaldsen) of A870 (Rome 1816). Inscribed: »A Thorwaldsen fecit«. H. 152,2 cm. See also A39. Purchased from Lord Ashburton, »The Grange«, Hampshire, in 1938.

A875 Hebe

Statue. Marble version (Thorvaldsen) of A37 (Rome 1806). Inscribed: »AT«. H. 156,5 cm. Purchased from William Randolph Hearst's collection in 1938.

A876 Ludvig Holberg

1684-1754. Danish playwright, historian, and philosopher.
Bust. Original plaster model. Nysø and Copenhagen 1839. H. 54,7 cm. See also A190. Entered in the inventory in 1938.

A877 Rosa Taddei

1799-1869. Italian improvisatrice.
Bust. Original plaster model. Rome 1826. H. 50,5 cm. Entered in the inventory in 1941.

A878 Cupid Asks Jupiter and Juno that the Rose May Be Queen of Flowers.

Relief. Plaster cast, probably of the sketch model for A394. H. 17 cm. W. 27 cm. Purchased 1941.

A879 Elisabeth (Elisa) von der Recke

1754-1833. German countess and poetess, née von Medem.
Bust. Original plaster model. Rome, probably 1805-06. H. 38,2 cm. Marble version, see A869. See also A852. Purchased 1944.

A880 Bertel Thorvaldsen's Head

Bozzetto. Terracotta. Fragment of the clay model for the self-portrait statue. H. 9 cm. See A163. Purchased 1944.

A881 Jacob Laurids Thrane

1785-1819. Danish architect.
Bust. Original plaster model. Rome c. 1806. H. 52,8 cm. Marble version, see Dep. 36. Entered in the inventory in 1946.

A882 Christ

Mask. Plaster cast of the face of the marble version of the Christ statue in The Church of Our Lady, Copenhagen. H. 44,5 cm. See A82. Entered in the inventory in 1946.

A883 Alexander I

1777-1825. Czar of Russia 1801.
Bust. Marble version (Thorvaldsen) of A715 (Warsaw 1820). Inscribed: »A. Thorvaldsen F. 1821.«, H. 67,8 cm. Purchased 1946.

A884 Horace Vernet

1789-1863. French painter.
Bust. Plaster cast, probably of the original plaster model A254, Rome 1832. H. 48,5 cm. Entered in the inventory in 1946.

A885 Jacob Loewy?

Died c. 1830. Austrian philanthropist.
Bust. Plaster cast. The original plaster model, Rome 1831. H. 51,6 cm. Entered in the inventory in 1946.

A886 Vittoria Caldoni

1807-?. Italian model from Albano.
Bust. Marble version (Thorvaldsen)
of A279 (Rome 1821). H. 52 cm.
Formerly in the collection of
P. O. Brøndsted. Purchased 1947.

A887 Ghazi 'L-Din Haidar

Padishah of Oudh, King of Oudh
1819-27.
Bust. Marble version (Thorvaldsen)
of A280 (Rome 1824). Inscribed:
»A. Thorvaldsen f. 1824«. H. 81,9
cm. Purchased 1949.

A888 Unknown Lady

Portrait medallion. Original plaster
model. Probably Copenhagen
c. 1796. D. 45 cm. The attribution
to Thorvaldsen unsure. Entered in
the inventory in 1950.

A889 Anne, Countess of Newburgh

C. 1762-1861. Née Webb, married
to A. J. Radcliffe, Earl of Newburgh.
Oval portrait medallion. Original
plaster model. Rome, probably
1818. H. 31,3 cm. W. 30,2 cm. Entered in the inventory in 1950.

A890 Georg Wilhelm Wilding

1790-1841. Married to Donna
Catharina de Branciforte, became
the Principe di Butera in 1814 after
the death of his father-in-law.
Bust. Marble version (Thorvaldsen)
of A275 (Rome 1815). Inscribed:
»AT«. H. 68,5 cm. Purchased 1950.

A891 Catharina de Branciforte

1768-1824. Née Branciforte e Pig-
natelli, daughter of the Principe de
Butera. Married in 1812 to Georg
Wilhelm Wilding. 1814 Principessa
di Butera.
Bust. Marble version (Thorvaldsen)
of A276 (Rome 1815). Inscribed:
»AT«. H. 70,5 cm. Purchased 1950.

A892 George Hilaro Barlow

1762-1848. Knighted 1803. Gov-
ernor General of India 1805-07.
Governor of Madras 1807-12.
Bust. Marble version (Thorvaldsen)
of A289 (Rome 1828). Inscribed:
»Thorvaldsen. F.« and
»S. G. H. Barlow«. H. 64 cm. Pre-
sented in 1950 by Victoria, Lady
Barlow, England.

A893 Thomson Henry Bonar

C. 1810-1817. Son of Colonel
Thomson Bonar.
Bust. Marble version (Thorvaldsen)
of the original plaster model
executed in 1817 in Rome. In-
scribed: »Thorvaldsen. Faciebat.
Romae. MDCCCXVII. Thomson.
Hen. Bonar/OB. Romae. Vix.
Ann. VII.« H. 56,2 cm. Purchased
1950.

A894 Cupid and the Graces

Statue. Marble version (Thorvaldsen) of A29 (Rome 1817-19) Inscribed: »Thorvaldsen Fecit«.
H. 172,7 cm. Purchased 1952.

A895 Shepherd Boy

Statue. Marble version (Thorvaldsen) of A177 (Rome 1817), probably executed 1822-25. Inscribed: »A. Thorwaldsen Fecit«. H. 148 cm. Purchased 1952.

A896 Holger Christian Reiersen

1746-1811. Danish Titular Councillor of State.
Portrait medallion. Original plaster model (?), bronzed. Inscribed: »B. Thorvald(sen) Fec 1793«. Copenhagen. D. 42 cm. Purchased 1953.

A897 Charlotte Kirstine Reiersen

1763-1810. Née Studsgaard, married to H. C. Reiersen.
Portrait medallion. Original plaster model (?), bronzed. Inscribed: »B. Thorvald(sen) Fec 1793«. Copenhagen. D. 42 cm. Purchased 1953.

A898 Jane Craufurd

C. 1798-1884. Daughter of the Scottish Baronet James Gregan Craufurd.
Bust. Marble version (Thorvaldsen) of A307 (Rome 1818). Inscribed: »AT«. H. 55 cm. Damaged by fire. Presented in 1953 by Brigadier General Sir Standish G. Craufurd.

A899 Mathias Saxtorph

1740-1800. Danish obstetrician.
Bust. Plaster cast of the marble bust in the Rigshospital, Copenhagen, commissioned from Thorvaldsen in 1800 shortly after Saxtorph's death. H. 52 cm. Purchased 1953.

A900 Edmund Bourke

1761-1821. Danish diplomat in Naples.
Bust. Executed in marble in Rome 1800 by Thorvaldsen, probably from a model by the Italian sculptor Domenico Cardelli (1767-1797). H. 45,1 cm. Presented in 1955 by Madame Wanda Krosinski, Brussels, in memory of her Danish grandmother, Madame Alix Dolez Castonier.

A901 Night with Her Children, Sleep and Death

Relief. Marble version (Thorvaldsen) of A369 (Rome 1815). Inscribed: »AT«. D. 80,5 cm. Presented in 1959 by Henrik Kaufmann, Danish Ambassador to the United States, in memory of his mother, Mathilde, née von Bernus (1866-1922), the reliefs having been in her childhood home, »Schlösschen«, Bockenheim, near Frankfurt-on-Main, for more than a century.

A902 Day: Aurora with the Genius of Light.

Relief. Marble version (Thorvaldsen) of A370 (Rome 1815). D. 80 cm. Presented in 1959 by Henrik Kaufmann, Danish Ambassador to the United States, in memory of his mother, Mathilde, née von Bernus (1866-1922), the reliefs having been in her childhood home, »Schlösschen«, Bockenheim, near Frankfurt-on-Main, for more than a century.

A903 Mathias Saxtorph

1740-1800. Danish obstetrician.
Oval portrait medallion. Probably
an original plaster model, bronzed.
Inscribed: »B. Thorvaldsen Fec.
1793«. Below the portrait: »Ham
Signer Moderen/Med Spæde Barn i
Favn/Og Froe Staar Manden Hos/
Og Signer Saxtorphs Navn/ XXIX
October MDCCLXXXXIII
Rahbek«. Copenhagen 1793.
H. 49,5 cm. W. 42,7 cm. Purchased
1962.

A904 Elisabeth Christine Saxtorph

1746-1823. Née Sibrand, married to
Mathias Saxtorph.
Oval portrait medallion. Probably
an original plaster model, bronzed.
Inscribed: »B. Thorvaldsen Fe(c)
1793«. Below the portrait: »Ey
Foed For Sig Alleene/XXIX Oc-
tober MDCCLXXXXIII Rahbek«.
Copenhagen 1793. H. 49,5 cm.
W. 42,7 cm. Purchased 1962.

A905 Night with Her Children, Sleep and Death

Relief. Marble version (Thorvaldsen) of A369 (Rome 1815) executed
1842. D. 79 cm. See also A901.
Purchased 1965.

A906 Day: Aurora with the Genius of Light.

Relief. Marble version of A370
(Rome 1815) executed in 1842 in
Thorvaldsens studio. D. 83,5 cm.
See also A902. Purchased 1965.

A907 Child's Head

Relief. Unfired clay. Fragment of
the clay model for A596 (Copenhagen 1838). H. 9 cm. Purchased
1966.

A908 Head of an Angel

Relief. Unfired clay. Fragment of
the clay model for A593 (Rome
1842). H. 12,3 cm. Purchased 1973.

A909 Napoleon I

1769-1821. Emperor of France
1804-14.
Bust. Original plaster model. Rome
c. 1830. H. 100 cm. Marble version,
see A732 and A867. See also A252.
Purchased 1974.

A910 Childhood – Spring

Relief. Marble version (Thorvaldsen) of A642 (Rome 1836). Inscribed: »Thorvaldsen F«. D. 68
cm. See also A638. Presented in
1977 by the estate of Dr. Bøje
Benzon.

A911 Cupid and the Graces

Statue. Plaster cast. The original
plaster model A29, Rome 1817-18.
H. 172 cm. See also A894. Entered
in the inventory in 1977.

A912 Cupid and the Graces

Statue, damaged. Plaster cast. The
original plaster model A29, Rome
1817-18. H. 167 cm. See also A894.
Entered in the inventory in 1977.

A913 Unknown Lady

Portrait medallion. Original plaster
model (?), painted. Inscribed:
»B. Thorvaldsen Fec. 179(5)«.
Copenhagen, probably 1795. D. 43
cm. Purchased 1982.

Dep. 21 The Seasons

Relief. Original plaster model. Copenhagen 1794. Modelled for Prince Frederik's (later Christian X's) Palace at Amalienborg, from a compostion by N. A. Abildgaard. H. 57,5 cm. W. 93,5 cm. On loan from the Royal Museum of Fine Arts.

Dep. 22 The Hours

Relief. Original plaster model. Copenhagen 1794. Modelled for Prince Frederik's (later Christian X's) Palace at Amalienborg, from a composition by N. A. Abildgaard. H. 57,5 cm. W. 94 cm. On loan from the Royal Museum of Fine Arts.

Dep. 23 Venus and Cupid

Sketch model. Plaster cast of the bozzetto in terracotta in the Hirschsprung Collection, Copenhagen. Modelled in 1827(?) in Rome. H. 23,7 cm. W. 40,8 cm. On loan from the Hirschsprung Collection.

Dep. 26 The Seasons

Relief. Plaster cast, painted, of the original plaster model Dep. 21, Copenhagen 1794. H. 58 cm. W. 93 cm.

Dep. 33 Frederik Carl Christian

1808-1863. Danish prince, from 1848 King Frederik VII of Denmark.
Bust. Marble version (Thorvaldsen) of A199 (Copenhagen 1820). Inscribed: »THORVALDSEN F.« H. 41,8 cm. On loan from Rosenborg Castle, Copenhagen.

Dep. 36 Jacob Laurids Thrane

1785-1819. Danish architect. Bust. Marble version of A881 (Rome c. 1806) completed in 1807 in Rome. H. 58,5 cm. On loan from Nordjyllands Kunstmuseum, Ålborg.

Catalogue of Paintings

Where not otherwise stated, the painting belonged to Thorvaldsen and came to the Museum according to the terms of his will.

If not otherwise specified, the medium is oil on canvas.

Abildgaard, Nicolai Abraham
Born Copenhagen 1743, died Spur-veskjul, Frederiksdal, 1809.

B 427 Cupid playing the lyre. Painted c. 1782. 28,5 × 23,4 cm. Purchased 1916.

Acquaroni,
See Aquaroni

Agricola, Filippo
Born Urbino 1776, died Rome 1857.

B 98 Portrait of Cardinal Ercole Consalvi, copied from Thomas Lawrence's full-length portrait of the Cardinal at Windsor Castle (1819). 54,9 × 41,9 cm.

Amerling, Friedrich von
Born Vienna 1803, died ibid. 1887.

B 105 Portrait of a Roman peasant. Signed »Fr. Amerling 1838«. 54,9 × 44,5 cm.

B435 Portrait of Thorvaldsen. Study for Cat. No. 353 in the Liechtenstein Gallery, Vienna, probably painted 1842. 49 × 39,5 cm.

Andersen, Christian Emil
Born Copenhagen 1817, died ibid. 1845.

B195 The Good Samaritan. Exhibited 1844. 112,5 × 94,2 cm.

Anesi, Paolo
Born Rome c. 1725, died ibid. 1766.

B33 Landscape. 49,7 × 64,1 cm. Attribution, formerly ascribed to Andrea Locatelli.

Anguissola, Sofonisba
Born Cremona 1527, died Palermo 1625.

B9 Portrait of a lady. Painted on slate. Diameter 11,8 cm.

Aquaroni, Antonio
Born Rome c. 1800, died ibid. 1874.

B58 Ponte Cestio in Rome. Painted 1836. 32 × 40,5 cm.

Baldi, Lazzaro
Born Pistoia c. 1623, died Rome 1703.

B27 Boreas and Oreithyia. 51 × 39,8 cm. Attribution.

Balsgaard, Carl Wilhelm

Born Copenhagen 1812, died ibid.
1893.

B311 Portrait of the sculptor Hermann Ernst Freund. Copy of a portrait by C. A. Jensen, painted in Rome 1819, in the Royal Museum of Fine Arts, Copenhagen (Inv. 1212). 11,8 × 8,4 cm.

B312 Portrait of Thorvaldsen. Copy from 1843 of a portrait by C. W. Eckersberg, painted in Rome 1814, in the Academy of Fine Arts, Copenhagen. 14,4 × 11,8 cm.

Barbieri, Giovanni Francesco (Guercino)

Born Cento 1591, died Bologna 1666.

B20 Young girl reading. 35,3 × 26,2 cm.

Baratta, Francesco

Born Genoa 1805, died ibid.
c. 1870.

B59 Italian winegrower and his daughter. 137,3 × 98,1 cm.

Barnekow, Robert Gabriel Adolph

Born Faaborg 1848, died New Zealand 1931.

B445 Room 42 in the Thorvaldsen Museum with Thorvaldsen's furniture. Signed »1878. R. B.«. 38 × 52 cm. Purchased 1951.

Bartolo, Taddeo di

See Taddeo di Bartolo

Bassano il Giovane, Francesco (da Ponte)

Born Bassano 1549 (?), died Venice 1592.

B10 Genre scene, in the background the Agony in the Garden (?). Signed »BASS.ˢ F.«. 94,2 × 131 cm.

Bassano, Jacopo, after

B25 The Descent of the Holy Ghost. Copy of a painting by Jacopo Bassano in the Museo Civico, Bassano. 60,2 × 32,7 cm.

Bassi, Giovanni Battista

Born Massa Lombarda 1784, died Rome 1852.

B60 Woodland scene with pool. Signed »G. B. Bassi f. sul vero 1816«. 96,8 × 119 cm.

B61 Road running between garden walls near Terni. Signed »G. B. Bassi f. sul vero 1820«. 49,1 × 61,5 cm.

B62 Forest track. Signed »G. B. Bassi studio sul vero 1824«. 68 × 61,5 cm.

B63 View of the ruins of the imperial palaces, Rome. Signed »G. B. Bassi f. Romæ«. 47,1 × 37,2 cm.

B86 See Pacetti, Michelangelo.

Bendz, Wilhelm Ferdinand

Born Odense 1804, died Vicenza 1832.

B197 Artists at an evening gathering in Finck's coffee-house, Munich. Signed »W. Bendz München 1832«. 94,8 × 136,6 cm.

Bianchi, Giovanni, after

B14 The Virgin and Child. Copy of a painting in the Church of Madonna della Ghiara, Reggio Emilia, by Giovanni Bianchi after a drawing by Lelio Orsi. Painted on copper. 18,3 × 15,1 cm.

Bloemen, Jan Franz van (Orizonte)

Born Antwerp 1662, died Rome 1749.

B49 Landscape. 73,2 × 60,2 cm. Attribution.

B50 Landscape. 37 × 48,4 cm. Attribution.

Blunck, Ditlev Conrad

Born Münsterdorf, Holstein, 1798, died Hamburg 1854.

B34 The Virgin and Child. Copy of a painting by Pietro Perugino in the Detroit Institute of Arts. 84,3 × 71,2 cm.

B35 Madonna del Granduca. Copy of a painting by Raphael in the Palazzo Pitti, Florence. 85 × 57,5 cm.

B 54 Portrait of a man. Copy of a portrait by Bartholomeus van der Helst. 69,3 × 52,3 cm.

B198 Noah and his family in the Ark. Signed »D. C. Blunck Roma 1835«. 69,3 × 90,2 cm.

B199 Danish artists at the Osteria La Gensola, Rome (To the right, Thorvaldsen). Signed »D. C. Blunck Roma 1837«. 74,5 × 99,4 cm.

B404 Two German doctors, Karl von Pfeuffer and Lorenz Melchior Geist. Signed »DCB« and inscribed »Zur dankbaren Erinnerung der mit Euch in Rom zusammen verlebten Monathe August und September 1837«. Painted on paper. 15 × 18,7 cm.

Dep. 32 Portrait of the architect M. G. Bindesbøll. Painted 1837. 29 × 22,3 cm. Lent by the Ny Carlsberg Glyptothek, Copenhagen.

Boesen, August Wilhelm

Born Vigerslev 1812, died Bologna 1857.

B200 Danish landscape. Signed »A. W. B.«. 32 × 44,5 cm.

Brill, Paul

Born Antwerp 1554, died Rome 1626.

B400 Mountain landscape. 77,5 × 109 cm. Attribution.

Bruegel (the Elder), Jan

Born Brussels 1568, died Antwerp 1625.

B44 Aeneas and the Cumaean Sibyl in the Underworld. (The painting was formerly called Hell). Painted on copper. 26,8 × 35,3 cm. Attribution.

B45 The Temptation of St. Anthony. Painted on copper. 19,6 × 24,8 cm. Attribution.

Buntzen, Heinrich Christian August
Born Kiel 1803, died Ordrup 1892.

B201 Oak trees by a pool. Signed »Heinr. Buntzen inv. et pinx. München 1840« 115,7 × 161,5 cm.

B202 Casa del Portinaio, formerly called the Villa of Raphael, in the gardens of the Villa Borghese, Rome. Signed »H. Buntzen pinx. Hafniæ 1843« Painted on paper. 25,5 × 32 cm.

B203 The manor house of Nysø, to the left Thorvaldsen in front of his studio. Signed »HB 1843«. 55,5 × 71,2 cm.

B204 Danish landscape. Signed »Heinrich Buntzen 1844«. 119 × 160,8 cm.

Bürkel, Heinrich
Born Pirmasens 1802, died Munich 1869.

B106 Scene in front of an Italian osteria. Signed »H. Bürkel. 1831«. 51 × 74,5 cm.

B107 The performing bears come to an Italian village. Signed »H. Bürkel Rom 1831«. 57,5 × 74,5 cm.

Bærentzen, Emilius Ditlev
Born Copenhagen 1799, died ibid. 1868.

B205 Portrait of the actress Johanne Luise Heiberg. Painted 1841. 122,5 × 94,5 cm.

Cades, Giuseppe
Born Rome 1750, died ibid. 1799.

B39 La Disputa del SS Sacramento. Copy of Raphael's fresco in the Stanza della Segnatura in the Vatican, Rome. 100,6 × 137,5 cm.

Caffi, Ippolito
Born Belluno 1809, died in the battle of Lissa 1866.

B64 *Moccoli* Evening in the Via del Corso during the carnival in Rome. Painted 1834. 38 × 47 cm.

B65 *La Girandola* fireworks from Castel Sant'Angelo during the Easter celebrations in Rome. Signed »Caffi«. 36,6 × 46,5 cm.

B66 A Venetian gala night. 22 × 29 cm.

Camuccini, Vincenzo
Born Rome 1771, died ibid. 1844.

B67 Christ blessing the children. Painted on wood, c. 1826. 22,9 × 34 cm.

Carracci, Annibale, after
B23 The penitent Mary Magdalene. Reduced copy of a painting by Annibale Carracci in the Galleria Doria Pamphili, Rome, Inv. No. 203. 32 × 41,9 cm.

Carstens, Asmus Jacob
Born S. Jürgen near Schleswig 1754, died Rome 1798.

See Catel, B299.

Carus, Carl Gustav

Born Leipzig 1789, died Dresden 1869.

B108 A prehistoric barrow by moonlight, Nobben on the island of Rügen. Painted on paper. 7,8 × 11,2 cm.

Castelli, Alessandro

Born Rome 1809, died ibid. 1902.

B68 Landscape. 29,4 × 44,5 cm.

Castello, Francesco da

Born in the Netherlands c. 1540, died Rome 1621.

B13 The Ecstasy of St. Francis. 131,1 × 96,8 cm. Attribution.

Catel, Franz

Born Berlin 1778, died Rome 1856.

B109 A Neapolitan fisherman and his family. 48,4 × 62,2 cm.

B110 A grotto in Mæcenas' Villa, Tivoli. 54,3 × 70 cm.

B111 Night piece, from the closing scene of »René« by Chateaubriand. 62,8 × 73,8 cm.

B112 Landscape at sunset. 15,7 × 24,1 cm.

B299 The Golden Age. Copy of a drawing by A. J. Carstens, painted 1812 by Catel (landscape) and John James Rubby (figures). 54,9 × 87,6 cm.

Chauvin, Pierre Athanase

Born Paris 1774, died Rome 1832.

B87 View of the gardens of the Villa Falconieri, Frascati. Signed »Chauvin à Frascati. 1810«. 62,2 × 74,5 cm.

B88 View of the gardens of the Villa d'Este, Tivoli. Signed »Chauvin à Tivoli 1811«. 62,8 × 73,8 cm.

B89 Grottaferrata in the Alban Hills. Signed »Chauvin 1811 à Grotta Ferrata«. 62,2 × 74,5 cm.

Cornelius, Peter

Born Düsseldorf 1783, died Berlin 1867.

B113 The Entombment of Christ. Painted on wood. 34 × 47,1 cm.

Correggio, Antonio Allegri,
after

B42 The marriage of St. Catherine. Copy of a painting by Correggio in the Louvre, Paris, Cat.No. 1117. 98,1 × 100,7 cm.

Dahl, Carl Michael

Born Faaborg 1812, died Copenhagen 1865.

B206 The frigate Thetis and the corvette Flora on the river Tagus. Painted 1844. 120,4 × 181 cm.

B207 Larsens Plads, the harbour of Copenhagen. Exhibited 1840. 54,9 × 70,6 cm.

B451 A. F. Tscherning showing two peasants the statue of Vulcan in the Thorvaldsen Museum. Purchased 1977. 38 × 38 cm.

Dahl, Johan Christian

Born Bergen 1788, died Dresden 1857.

B128 See Koch, Joseph Anton

B177 The Bay of Naples by moon-light. Signed »J. Dahl 1821«. 49,7 × 68 cm.

B178 The Bay of Naples by moon-light. Signed »J. Dahl 1821«. 34 × 48,4 cm.

B179 Vesuvius in eruption. Moon-light. Signed »Dahl 1821«. 24,8 × 39,8 cm.

B180 Grotto by the Bay of Naples. Moonlight. Signed »Dahl Juni 1821«. 22,2 × 33,4 cm.

B181 St. Peter's Square by moon-light. Signed »Dahl 1821«. 37,9 × 30,1 cm.

B182 Country road near La Storta, Italy. Signed »d. 7. april 1821«. 22,9 × 32,7 cm.

B183 A waterfall, Italy. Signed »Rom d. 26. Juni 1821«. 36,6 × 47,1 cm.

B184 Norwegian mountain land-scape with waterfall. Signed »Dahl 1821«. 98,8 × 137,3 cm.

B185 Norwegian landscape, Jor-dalsnuten. Signed »Dahl 1821«. 35,3 × 47,1 cm.

B186 Norwegian mountain valley. Signed »Dahl Mai 1821« (or 1827). 96,8 × 134,6 cm.

B187 The seaward approach to Copenhagen. Signed »Dahl 1830«. 40,5 × 55,5 cm.

B188 The coast at Laurvig, Nor-way. Signed »Dahl 1840«. Painted on paper. 7,8 × 13,1 cm.

B189 Landscape from Telemark, Norway. Signed »Dahl 1840«. Painted on paper. 7,8 × 13,1 cm.

Dandini, Pier

Born Florence 1646, died ibid. 1712.

B17 The penitent Mary Magdalene. 51,7 × 44,5 cm. Attribution.

Diofebi, Francesco

Born Narni 1781, died Rome 1851.

B69 Penitents in a Roman church. Signed »F. Diofebj f.«. 46,5 × 37,9 cm.

B70 The side steps from the Capitol to the church of S. Maria in Aracoeli, Rome. Signed »Diofebi f. 1825«. 99,4 × 73,8 cm.

B71 The ruined Temple of Mars Ul-tor, Rome. Signed »Diofebj f. 1826«. 61,5 × 47,7 cm.

B72 St. Joseph's Day (March 19) in Rome. Signed »Diofebi f. 1832«. 61,5 × 74,5 cm.

B73 The opening of Raphael's grave in 1833, to the right Thorvaldsen as representative of the Accademia di San Luca, Rome. Signed »F. Diofebi f. 1836«. 54,9 × 70 cm.

B74 The approach to the Villa Borghese, Rome. Signed »Diofebi f. 1838«. 37,9 × 47,1 cm.

B75 Children playing in a Roman street. Signed »Diofebi f. 1838. 37,2 × 47,1 cm.

B76 Italian monastery in the mountains. Signed »Diofebi f. 1839«. 37,2 × 47,1 cm.

B77 Night piece, nuns in a convent. Signed »Diofebj«. 36,6 × 47,1 cm.

Dreyer, Dankvart Christian Magnus

Born Assens 1816, died Barløse 1852.

B208 View of the coast near Aarhus. Signed »Dreyer«. Painted c. 1839. 93,5 × 129,4 cm.

Dutch School

17th century.

B47 Man with a wine-glass. Painted on copper. 13,7 × 11,1 cm.

Eckersberg, Christoffer Wilhelm

Born Blaakrog, Varnæs, 1783, died Copenhagen 1853.

B209 Sleeping woman in antique dress. Fragment of a painting »The Dream of Alcyone« (Ovid's Metamorphoses, XI, 410-748). Signed »Roma 1813«. 44,5 × 39,2 cm.

B210 Female harvester in antique dress. Fragment of a painting »Vertumnus and Pomona« Painted in Rome 1813-16. 36 × 19,6 cm.

B211 A Roman beggar. Painted in Rome 1815. 29,4 × 20,9 cm.

B212 Socrates expounding a proposition to Alcibiades. Painted in Rome 1813-16. 32,7 × 24,1 cm.

B213 Hector's farewell to Andromache. Painted in Rome 1813-16. 49,1 × 34,6 cm.

B214 St. Peter's Square. Painted in Rome 1813-16. 31,4 × 26,8 cm.

B215 The Virgin and Child, enthroned on the clouds. Free copy of the upper part of Raphaels's »Madonna di Foligno« in the Vatican. Painted in Rome 1816. 35,3 × 28,2 cm.

B216 Portrait of Frederik VI. Replica of a portrait made in 1820. Painted 1839. Signed »Ætatis L. MDCCCXX. E. fecit«. 59,5 × 51 cm.

B217 Thorvaldsen's arrival in the Copenhagen roadstead, September 17th 1838. Painted 1839. Signed »E«. 71,9 × 96,2 cm.

B405 The Colosseum. Painted in Rome 1813-16. 32 × 25,5 cm.

B406 Portrait of a Lady, probably the Roman model Maddalena. Copy, probably by a pupil, of a painting from 1814 in the Hirschsprung Collection, Copenhagen. 26,5 × 19,3 cm. Presented to the Museum 1868.

B419 Portrait of Thorvaldsen. Replica of a portrait from 1820 in a private collection. 50,3 × 40,3 cm. Presented to the Museum 1855, entered the collections in 1871.

Eggers, Carl.

Born Neustrelitz 1787, died ibid. 1863.

B36 La Madonna del garofano. Copy of a painting, formerly ascribed to Raphael. Painted on wood. 28,8 × 23,5 cm.

B37 The violin player. Copy of a painting by Sebastiano del Piombo in the E. de Rothschild Collection, Paris. 70,6 × 54,9 cm.

Eggink, Johann Leberecht

Born Kurland 1787, died Mitau 1867.

B38 The vision of Ezekiel. Copy of a painting by Raphael in the Palazzo Pitti, Florence, Cat.No. 174. Painted on wood. 40,5 × 29,4 cm.

Elsasser, Friedrich August

Born Berlin 1810, died Rome 1845.

B114 View from the ancient theatre in Taormina. Painted 1838. Signed »A. Elsasser Roma«. 68 × 102,6 cm.

Fearnley, Thomas

Born Frederikshald 1802, died Munich 1842.

B190 Norwegian landscape, Marumfoss. Signed »Th. Fearnley 1833«. 124,9 × 174,6 cm.

B191 The sea at Palermo. Signed »TF Palermo. 24. Juny 1833«. 18,3 × 25,5 cm.

B192 Capri viewed from Sorrento. Signed »TF Sorrent. 28. Aug. 33« (1833). 15,1 × 22,2 cm.

B193 View of Elsinore, summer. Signed »Th. Fearnley 1833«. 74,5 × 100 cm.

B194 View of Elsinore, winter. Signed »Th. Fearnley 1833«. 74,5 × 100 cm.

Ferrarese School

Late 16th century.

B7 The Virgin with her family. 56,2 × 75,4 cm. Stylistically close to Sigismondo Scarsella.

Fiorentino,

See Pseudo-Pier Francesco Fiorentino

Fiorenzo di Lorenzo

Born c. 1440, died 1522/5. Active in Umbria.

B4 Two panels from an altar-piece, showing St. Eligius and John the Baptist. On the back a circle inscribed in a rhombus and in the corners an axe, a hammer and two knives. Tempera on wood. 62,8 × 45,8 cm. Attribution.

Fioroni, Luigi

Born S. Fiora 1795, died Rome 1864.

B78 Evening scene at a Roman osteria by the Piazza della Trinità dei Monti. Signed »Luigi Fironi fece 1830«. 74,5 × 100 cm.

B79 Pope Pius VIII carried in procession through the colonnade of St. Peter's. Rome. Painted 1829-30. 50,3 × 62,2 cm.

Flemish School

17th century.

B51 A ferry. 41,9 × 60,2 cm. Formerly ascribed to »the manner of A. F. Boudewyns and Peeter Bout«.

B52 Road beside a river. 41,9 × 60,2 cm. Formerly ascribed to »the manner of A. F. Boudewyns and Peeter Bout«.

B53 Crowd scene. 40,5 × 52,3 cm. Formerly ascribed to »the manner of A. F. Boudewyns and Peeter Bout«.

Flor, Ferdinand

Born Hamburg 1793, died Rome 1881.

B115 Portrait of Elisa Paulsen, Thorvaldsen's daughter. Painted 1838. 74,5 × 62,8 cm.

Foltz, Philipp von

Born Bingen 1805, died Munich 1877.

B116 Sleeping Italian beggar girl in a Roman church. Signed »Foltz inv. 1836 Rom«. 74,5 × 62,2 cm.

B117 Composition sketch illustrating Johann Ludwig Uhland's poem »Des Sängers Fluch«. Signed »Foltz inv. Roma 1837«. 79,8 × 60,8 cm.

Francesco, Beniamino de

Born Naples, died Dinard, St. Malo, 1869.

B80 Italian landscape. Signed »De Francesco 1836«. 41,2 × 60,2 cm.

B81 Italian landscape with Æneas and the Cumaean Sibyl. Signed »De Francesco 1838«. Painted on wood. 71,9 × 90,2 cm.

Friedlænder, Julius

Born Copenhagen 1810, died ibid. 1861.

B218 Scene in a fishing hamlet (Taarbæk) in Zealand. Signed »J. F. 1839«. 53,6 × 64,1 cm.

Galster, Henrik Ludvig

Born Nørre Sundby 1826, died Copenhagen 1901.

B439 Portrait of Thorvaldsen. Reduced copy of Horace Vernet's portrait (B95). Signed »H. L. Galster«. Painted on ivory. 8,3 × 8,6 cm. Presented to the Museum 1935.

Gazzarini, Tommaso

Born Leghorn 1790, died Florence 1853.

B82 The infant Christ. Painted 1822. 17,7 × 24,8 cm.

Gegenbauer, Joseph Anton

Born Wangen 1800, died Rome 1876.

B314 Hercules and Omphale. Painted 1826. Fresco, transferred to canvas. 202,7 × 155,6 cm.

German School (?)
18th century.

B57 A shoemaker's shop. 62,2 × 73,8 cm. When in Thorvaldsen's possession ascribed to William Hogarth.

German School (?)
18th century.

B414 Portrait of a man. Oval miniature. 2,4 × 2 cm.

Gertner, Johan Vilhelm
Born Copenhagen 1818, died ibid. 1871.

B 430 Thorvaldsen in his studio. Painted on wood, c. 1839. 33 × 24,5 cm. Presented to the Museum 1923.

Dep. 35 Thorvaldsen modelling the bust of Adam Oehlenschläger. Painted 1842. 121 × 83 cm. Lent by Nordjyllands Kunstmuseum, Ålborg.

Gimignani, Giacinto
Born Pistoia 1611, died Rome 1681.

B21 The Virgin and Child. 67,4 × 51 cm. Attribution.

Giovannini, Vincenzo
Born Todi 1816, died Rome 1868.

B96 A chemist in his laboratory. 73,2 × 98,1 cm.

Glowacki, Jan Nepomucen
Born Cracow 1802, died ibid. 1847.

B174 Tyrolean (or Bavarian) landscape. Signed »I. Nep. Glowacki Roma 1835«. Painted on paper. 34,6 × 45,1 cm.

Gorawski, Apollinari,
see: Horawski, Apollinarij

Grove, Fritz Nordahl
Born Copenhagen 1822, died ibid. 1885.

B219 View from Baunebjerg by Horsens Fjord. Exhibited 1843. 50,1 × 76,5 cm.

Gudin, Théodore
Born Paris 1802, died Boulogne-sur-Seine 1880.

B90 The coast near Naples. Signed »T. Gudin Rome 1837«. 40,5 × 61,5 cm.

Guérard, Bernhard von
Born Düsseldorf, died Naples 1836.

B447 Portrait of Thorvaldsen. Replica of a painting from 1831 in the Museo di Capodimonte, Naples. Signed »B. Ch. Guérard 1834«. Painted on wood. 19,4 × 15,2 cm.

Guercino,
see Barbieri, Giovanni Francesco

Hansen, Carl Christian Constantin

Born Rome 1804, died Copenhagen 1880.

B220 View of the Temple of Poseidon at Pæstum. Painted 1839. 30,1 × 34 cm.

B415 Portrait of the architect M. G. Bindesbøll. Signed »Const. H. 1849«. 118 × 95 cm. Commissioned by the board of directors of the Thorvaldsen Museum.

B416 Portrait of Jonas Collin, titular Privy Councillor, Chairman of the Thorvaldsen Museum Committee. Signed »Const. H. 1851«. 105,8 × 84,5 cm. Presented to the Museum 1851.

B442 View of the Thorvaldsen Museum. Signed »CH. 58« (1858). 36,3 × 43,8 cm. Presented to the Museum 1938.

Harder, Johannes (Hans)

Born Copenhagen 1792, died Sorø 1873.

B221 Landscape with the Mill at Bromme near Sorø. Painted on wood. 30,1 × 43,2 cm.

Heideck, Karl Wilhelm von

Born Saaralben 1788, died Munich 1861.

B118 Scene from the defence of a Spanish town during a guerrilla war. Signed »C. v. Hdk p^t $\frac{4}{1841}$«. 71,2 × 92,8 cm.

Hellesen, Lars Julius August

Born Copenhagen 1823, died ibid. 1877.

B222 Danish landscape. Signed »Julius Hellesen 1843«. 94,8 × 126,1 cm.

B223 The coast at the fishing hamlet of Flade near Frederikshavn. Signed »jH. 1842«. 22,2 × 35,3 cm.

Henning, Adolph

Born Berlin 1809, died ibid. 1900.

B119 Portrait of the model Fortunata Segatori from Subiaco as poetess. Painted between 1833 and 1835. 46,5 × 46,5 cm.

Henriques, Salomon (Sally) Ruben

Born Copenhagen 1815, died ibid. 1886.

B407 Portrait of a sailor. Painted 1840. 50,7 × 46,8 cm.

Hensel, Wilhelm

Born Trebbin 1794, died Berlin 1861.

B437 Portrait of Thorvaldsen. Signed on the back »W. Hensel ad viv. pinxt.«. 54,3 × 43,8 cm. Presented to the Museum 1934.

Hering, George Edwards

Born London 1805, died ibid. 1879.

B120 A street in Smyrna. Signed »G. H. 33« (1833). 42,5 × 37,2 cm.

Heuss, Franz Eduard

Born Oggersheim 1808, died Bodenheim 1880.

Dep. 2. Portrait of Thorvaldsen. Signed: »Heuss 1834«, on the back: »Hanc Alberti Thorvaldsen effigiem Romæ pinxit anno 1834 Ed. Heuss«. 74,5 × 62,2 cm. Lent by the Ny Carlsberg Clyptotek.

Holbech, Niels Peter

Born at sea 1804, died Karlshamn 1889.

B224 A young Italian woman with her children and an old woman spinning, Nettuno. Signed »NPH 1831«. 62,2 × 50,3 cm.

B225 A pilgrim sitting by a fountain in the Via dell' Arco Scuro, Rome. Probably painted between 1830 and 1834. 64,1 × 49,7 cm.

Hopfgarten, August

Born Berlin 1807, died ibid. 1896.

B122 The miracle of St. Elizabeth. Signed »A. Hopfgarten Rom 1832«. 62,2 × 44,5 cm.

Horawski, Apollinarij Hilarjevitsch

Born Minsk 1833, died St. Petersburg 1900.

B441 Portrait of Thorvaldsen. Copy painted 1852 after a portrait by Orest Kiprenski from 1833 in the Hermitage, Leningrad. 65 × 54,5 cm. Presented to the Museum 1937.

Hornemann, Christian

Born Copenhagen 1765, died ibid. 1844.

B310 Portrait of Thorvaldsen. Signed »Hornemann«. Painted on ivory. 10,9 × 8,2 cm.

Høyer, Christian Fædder

Born Rerslev near Roskilde 1775, died Copenhagen 1855.

B226 Cupid received by Anacreon. From Anacreontea, Song 3. Probably painted between 1808 and 1811. 74,5 × 98,8 cm.

B408 Ossian carrying his dead brother Fillan, followed by Fingal's dog Bran. From Songs of Ossian, Temora 6. 51 × 66,5 cm.

B409 The metamorphosis of Lucius. From Apuleius' The Golden Ass. 51 × 68 cm.

Ingemann, Lucie Marie

Born Copenhagen 1792, died Sorø 1868.

B410 A gardener. 35,5 × 31,5 cm.

B429 The Apotheosis of Thorvaldsen. 77,5 × 67 cm. Presented to the Museum 1922.

Italian School

16th century.

B8 Portrait of a man. Painted on wood. 44,5 × 32,7 cm.

Italian School

17th century.

B19 The Virgin and Child with St. Martha. 45,8 × 37,9 cm.

Italian School

17th century.

B22 St. Joseph with the flowering rod. 62,8 × 48,4 cm.

Italian School

17th century.

B24 The Holy Family. 95,5 × 72,6 cm.

Italian School

17th century.

B26 The dream of St. Joseph. 69,3 × 90,2 cm.

Italian School

17th century.

B30 Buildings along a coastline. Supraporte painting. 23,5 × 109,3 cm.

Italian School

17th century.

B306 The ecstasy of St. Francis. Painted on leather. 19,6 × 15,7 cm.

Italian School

16th century?

B313 Head of a saint. Painted on chalk. 28,8 × 21,5 cm.

Jensen, Carl Vilhelm Marius

Born Ringsted 1819, died Liljedal, Ørslev, 1882.

B228 The Manor of Gisselfeld, Zealand. Signed »C. V. Jensen 1839«. 50,3 × 74,5 cm.

Jensen, Christian Albrecht

Born Bredsted near Husum (Holstein) 1792, died Copenhagen 1870.

B227 Portrait of the flower painter Claudius Ditlev Fritzsch. Painted c. 1835. 24,1 × 18,9 cm.

B432 Portrait of Baroness Christine Stampe, née Dalgas. Signed »C. A. Jensen 1827«. 64,2 × 50,8 cm. Presented to the Museum 1924.

B433 Portrait of Thorvaldsen. Signed »C. A. Jensen pinxit 1839«. 28,8 × 22,8 cm. Presented to the Museum 1926.

B444 Portrait of the poet Ludvig Bødtcher. Signed »C. A. Jensen 1836«. 36 × 28,8 cm. Presented to the Museum 1942.

Jensen, Johan Laurentz

Born Gentofte 1800, died Copenhagen 1856.

B230 Flowers in a vase on a marble tabletop. Signed »I. L. Jensen 1833«. 22,2 × 28,8 cm.

B231 Fruit on a marble tabletop. Signed »I. L. Jensen 1833«. 24,1 × 32,7 cm.

B232 Flowers in an antique vase. Signed »I. L. Jensen Roma 1834«. 61,5 × 50,3 cm.

B233 Still life on a kitchen tabletop. Signed »I. L. Jensen Roma 1835«. 90,9 × 75,2 cm.

B234 Flowers in an antique vase. Signed »I. L. Jensen 1838«. 90,2 × 71,9 cm.

B236 White lilies and roses. Signed »1843«. Painted on wood. 58,8 × 42,5 cm.

Jensen, Johannes

Born Copenhagen 1818, died ibid. 1873.

B229 Portrait of an old sailor. Signed »Joh:Jensen 1843«. 39,8 × 32,7 cm.

B434 Portrait of Thorvaldsen. 14,9 × 12,7 cm. Presented to the Museum 1928.

B436 Portrait of Thorvaldsen. 12,9 × 12 cm. Purchased 1933.

Juel, Jens

Born Funen 1745, died Copenhagen 1802.

B237 View of the Little Belt from Hindsgavl, Funen. Probably painted c. 1800. 42 × 62,5 cm.

B238 View of the Little Belt from a hill near Middelfart, Funen. Probably painted c. 1800. 42,3 × 62,5 cm.

B239 View from Veyrier over Lake Geneva towards the Jura mountains. Painted between 1777 and 1779. 116,4 × 86,9 cm.

B315 Portrait of Wilhelmine Bertouch, Lady-in-Waiting. Pastel. 52,3 × 39,2 cm.

Juel, Jens, after

B411 Portrait of the artist's mother, Vilhelmine Elisabeth Juel. Copy of a painting by Juel, probably exhibited 1794, in the Ny Carlsberg Glyptotek, Copenhagen, Inv. No. 900. 47 × 39 cm.

Kaufmann, Hermann

Born Hamburg 1808, died ibid. 1889.

B123 Tyrolean roadside inn. Signed »H. Kaufmann 1843«. 36 × 49,1 cm.

Kiprenski, Orest

Born Koporje 1773, died Rome 1836.

B175 Portrait of an Armenian priest. On the back a study of the male nude. 74,5 × 58,8 cm.

Kiærskou, Frederik Christian

Born Copenhagen 1805, died ibid. 1891.

B240 The Road from Reichenhall to Ramsau in Bavaria. Signed »F. C. Kierskou 1846«. 76,5 × 62,8 cm.

Klenze, Leo von

Born Schladen am Harz 1784, died Munich 1864.

B124 The harbour at Pirano, Istria. Signed »L. v. K«. Painted 1831. 62,8 × 78,5 cm.

Kloss, Friedrich Theodor

Born Brunswick 1802, died Copenhagen 1876.

B241 Approach to Copenhagen by sea. Signed »T Kloss 1838«. 34 × 50,3 cm.

Koch, Joseph Anton

Born Obergiebeln 1768, died Rome 1839.

B125 Apollo among the Thessalian shepherds. Signed »J. K.«. Painted 1834-35. 79,1 × 115,7 cm.

B126 Italian landscape with bridge over river, Terni. Signed »J. Koch f.«. Painted on wood, around 1830. 35,3 × 49,7 cm.

B127 Landscape from Olevano, to the right a self-portrait. Signed »J. Koch«. Painted on wood, ca. 1823. 35,3 × 47,7 cm.

B128 Lauterbrunnertal near Unterseen with a view of the Jungfrau. Probaly painted 1821 in collaboration with J. C. Dahl, who inserted the shepherd with his goats. 74,5 × 98,1 cm.

B129 Noah's sacrifice after the Flood. Signed »G. Koch Tyrolese 1815«. Painted on wood. 18,9 × 23,5 cm.

B158 See Schick, Gottlieb.

Koop, Andreas Ludvig

Born Copenhagen 1792, died Rome 1849.

B168 Portrait of Thorvaldsen. Copy painted 1828 after a portrait from 1823 by Karl Begas. 103,3 × 73,2 cm.

Krafft, Johan August

Born Altona 1798, died Rome 1829.

B242 Carnival gaiety in a Roman street. Signed »Augt. Krafft 1828«. 32,7 × 42,5 cm.

Küchler, Albert

Born Copenhagen 1803, died Rome 1886. Became a monk in 1851 as Fra Pietro.

B243 The death of Correggio, scene from Act V of Adam Oehlenschläger's tragedy »Correggio«. Signed »A. Küchler 1834«. 83,7 × 74,5 cm.

B244 Domestic scene by Lake Nemi. Signed »A. Küchler. Rom 1837«. 95,5 × 81,1 cm.

B245 Colonel and Mrs Paulsen, Thorvaldsen's son-in-law and daughter, with their two children. Signed »A. Küchler Roma 1838«. 71,9 × 64,8 cm.

B246 Roman peasants buying a hat for their little son, who is to be an abbate. Signed »A. Küchler 1840«. 75,9 × 92,8 cm.

B247 A young abbate recites his lesson to his sister. Signed »A. Küchler«. Painted c. 1838. 44,5 × 37,9 cm.

La Bouère, Tancrède de

Born La Bouère, Jallais, 1801, died Grenoble 1881.

B91 The coast by the Pontine marshes. In the foreground buffaloes. Signed »Labouère à Rome 1838«. 100,7 × 168 cm.

Landesio, Eugenio

Born 1809, died 1879. Active in Rome.

B83 Italian landscape. Signed »E. Landesio F. Roma 1838«. 74,4 × 92,1 cm.

Larsen, Peter Julius

Born Copenhagen 1818, died Rome 1852.

B248 Portrait of an old sailor. Signed »P. L. 1840«. 37,2 × 30,8 cm.

B452 Interior from the Academy of Fine Arts, Copenhagen, with works by Thorvaldsen. Signed »PJ Larsen 1837«. 71,5 × 53 cm. Purchased 1977.

Lazzarini, Giovanni

Born 1769, died 1834. Active in Rome and Lucca.

B84 The Roman aqueduct Aqua Vergine in the courtyard of No. 12 Via del Nazareno. Painted by two artists. Signed »J.(G)... et Lazzarini Amici f-nt Romæ 1823«. 60,8 × 73,8 cm.

B97 The choir of the Capuchin Monastery near the Piazza Barberini, Rome. Copy of a painting by François Marius Granet. 47,7 × 36,6 cm.

Libert, Georg Emil

Born Copenhagen 1820, died ibid. 1908.

B249 View of the Sound from Langelinie near Copenhagen. Signed »G. E. Libert 1839«. 94,2 × 126,1 cm.

B250 Moors near Aalborg. Signed »G. E. Libert 1839«. 65,4 × 102,6 cm.

Lindau, Dietrich Wilhelm

Born Dresden 1799, died Rome 1862.

B130 Peasants at Monte Mario on their way to Rome. Signed »Dietrich Lindau Roma 1826«. 52,3 × 76,2 cm.

B131 A *Saltarello* being danced in a Roman osteria. Signed »Dietrich Lindau 1827«. 50,3 × 71,9 cm.

B424 Portrait of Thorvaldsen. Signed »Lindau f. Romæ«. Painted on paper, c. 1827. 17,2 × 14,5 cm.

Löhr, Franz Conrad

Born 1735, died 1812. Active in Hamburg.

B438 Portrait of a man. According to tradition a portrait of Gotskalk Thorvaldsen, Thorvaldsen's father. Signed »F. C. Löhr pinxit 1788«. 67 × 53 cm. Purchased 1934.

Lorenzo, Fiorenzo di

see Fiorenzo di Lorenzo

Lorenzo Monaco,

see Monaco, Lorenzo

Lund, Johan Ludvig Gebhard

Born Kiel 1777, died Copenhagen 1867.

B251 St. Anne teaching the Virgin to read (Friederike Brun and Mimmi Zoëga). Painted on wood, 1818. 41,2 × 32,7 cm.

B252 Italian landscape. Painted on wood. 28,8 × 22,9 cm.

B301 Portrait of a lady. 45,8 × 40,3 cm. Attribution.

B412 Sophienholm, the manor house of Constantin Brun. Painted on an iron plate. 26,4 × 21,3 cm.

B448 Portrait of Orsola Polverini Narlinghi, Thorvaldsen's landlady in Rome 1800-04. 14,5 × 11,5 cm. Presented to the Museum 1966.

Lund, Troels

Born Copenhagen 1802, died ibid. 1867.

B300 Portrait of Jørgen Bentzen (1742-1822), porter and model at the Academy of Fine Arts, Copenhagen. 55 × 50 cm.

Lundbye, Johan Thomas

Born Kalundborg 1818, died Bedsted 1848.

B253 Landscape at Arresø, looking towards the sand-dunes at Tisvilde. Signed »JTL 1838«. 94,2 × 125,5 cm. Won by Thorvaldsen at the Art Society, Copenhagen, in 1839.

B254 View from Vinderød towards Høbjerg near Frederiksværk, with the home af Lundbye's parents. Painted 1839 as companion piece to B253. 94,2 × 125,5 cm.

B255 Dolmen at Raklev, Røsnæs. Signed »JTL Mai 1839«, 66,7 × 88,9 cm.

Lunde, Anders Christian

Born Copenhagen 1809, died ibid. 1886.

B256 View of Frederiksberg Palace from the vicinity of Ladegaardsvej, Copenhagen. Exhibited 1840. 42,5 × 63,4 cm.

Læssøe, Thorald

Born Frederikshavn 1816, died Copenhagen 1878.

B257 Valløby Church, Zealand. Signed »Thorald Læssøe 1839«. 73,8 × 109,3 cm.

Magnus, Eduard

Born Berlin 1799, died ibid. 1872.

B132 Portrait of Thorvaldsen in his working clothes. Painted c. 1828. 62,8 × 49,7 cm.

Markó, Carl (Károly)

Born Lócse, Hungary, 1791, died Antella near Florence 1860.

B169 View of Lake Nemi and Monte Cavo. Signed »C. Markó 1834«. 74,5 × 99,4 cm.

B170 Landscape with nymphs. Signed »S. Markó 1834«. 26,8 × 29,4 cm.

B171 Landscape with nymphs bathing. Signed »C. Markó 1834«. 26,8 × 29,4 cm.

B172 Italian mountain scene, women by a fountain. Signed »C. Markó Romæ 1836«. 34 × 45,8 cm.

B173 Italian mountain scene, wanderers on a road. Signed »C. Markó Romæ«. 1836(?). 34 × 45,8 cm.

Marstrand, Wilhelm Nicolai

Born Copenhagen 1810, died ibid. 1873.

B258 October Festival evening outside the walls of Rome. Signed »W. Marstrand Roma 1839«. 90,9 × 123 cm.

B420 *Abbate* jesting with two young girls. Marstrand's last work, painted March 15, 1873. 42 × 55,3 cm. Presented to the Museum 1873.

B421 Portrait of Just Mathias Thiele, Thorvaldsen's biographer. 87,3 × 70,5 cm. Purchased 1874.

Dep. 25 Portrait of the architect M. G. Bindesbøll. Signed »W. M. 1844«. 20 × 15 cm. Lent by the Royal Museum of Fine Arts.

Martens, Hans Ditlev Christian

Born Kiel 1795, died ibid. 1864.

B259 The Antique Room at the Academy of Fine Arts, Copenhagen. Signed »H. D. C. Martens pinxit 1824«. 92,8 × 74,5 cm.

B260 St. Peter's from the Via Sacra, north of Rome. Painted on paper. 76,5 × 54,3 cm.

B261 The Capitol in Rome, from the colonnade of the Palazzo dei Conservatori. 76,5 × 54,3 cm.

B262 The house of Michelangelo in Rome. Signed »H. D. C. Martens Roma 1833«. 57,5 × 71,9 cm.

Dep. 18 Pope Leo XII visits Thorvaldsen's studios near the Piazza Barberini, Rome, on St. Luke's Day (October 18th), 1826. Signed »H. D. C. Martens. Roma«. Painted 1830. 100 × 138 cm. Lent by the Royal Museum of Fine Arts.

Melbye, Daniel Herman Anton

Born Copenhagen 1818, died Paris 1875.

B263 A calm morning at sea. Signed »A. Melbye 1840«. 47,1 × 57,5 cm.

B264 Dutch koff and ship of the line in a moderate breeze. Signed »Anton Melbye - 1840«. 70,6 × 95,5 cm.

B265 Fishing-boats in the Channel. Signed »Anton Melbye 1844«. 19,6 × 27,5 cm.

Meyer, Ernst

Born Altona 1797, died Rome 1861.

B266 A Roman street letter-writer reading a letter aloud to a young girl. Signed »18 EM 29«. 62,2 × 69,3 cm.

B267 A Roman street letter-writer writing a letter for a young girl. Signed »E. M.«, on the letter the date 1827. 62,2 × 69,3 cm.

B268 A Capri fisherman. Signed »E. Meier Rom«. Painted 1844 (?) and purchased after the death of Thorvaldsen. 45,8 × 59,5 cm.

B269 A Neapolitan fisherman at his door. Signed »E Meyer«. 49,7 × 39,8 cm.

B270 A Capri fisherman with his net. 27,5 × 39,8 cm.

B271 The courtyard of the Franciscan monastery at Amalfi. 47,7 × 20,9 cm.

B272 A Franciscan monk, the hermit of the Colosseum in Rome. 32 × 22,2 cm.

B273 Half-length portrait of a young Franciscan. Signed »E. Meier«. 26,8 × 22,2 cm.

Mohr, Johannes Georg Paul

Born Bordesholm, Holstein, 1808, died Munich 1843.

B274 Winter landscape from Bordesholm. Signed »J. Mohr Kopenhagen 1840«. 79,1 × 112,5 cm.

B275 Landscape from Ischldorf, Bavaria. Signed »Mohr 1840«. 81,1 × 118,3 cm.

Monaco, Lorenzo

Born Siena c. 1370, died Florence c. 1425.

B1 The Virgin and Child. Tempera on wood. 22,2 × 18,3 cm. Part of a diptychon, the other part of which is probably a St. Jerome in the Rijksmuseum, Amsterdam, Inv. No. 1641 BI.

Monies, David

Born Copenhagen 1812, died ibid. 1894.

B418 Kitchen interior. Signed »D. Monies 1861« 62,7 × 74,5 cm. Purchased 1864.

Montanini, Pietro

Born Perugia 1625, died ibid. 1689.

B29 A tree struck by lightning. 65,4 × 49,1 cm. Attribution, formerly ascribed to Salvator Rosa.

Müller, Adam August

Born Copenhagen 1811, died ibid. 1844.

B276 Christ and the Evangelists. Signed »Adam Müller Rom 1842«. 251,1 × 156,9 cm.

Møller, Jens Peter

Born Faaborg 1783, died Copenhagen 1854.

B277 Landscape at Svendborg Sound. Signed »J. P. M. 1843«. 56,9 × 73,8 cm.

B278 The town of Svendborg, Funen. Signed »I. P. M. 1844«. 48,7 × 71,9 cm.

Neergaard, Hermania Sigvardine

Born Copenhagen 1799, died Aldershvile, Bagsværd, 1875.

B279 Flowers in a glass. Signed »H. Neergaard 1842«. 51 × 41,9 cm.

Nerly, Friedrich

Born Erfurt 1807, died Venice 1878.

B133 Buffaloes dragging a block of marble for Thorvaldsen through the Roman Campagna. Signed »F. Nerly fece«. Replica of a painting from 1831 in Schwerin. 74,5 × 99,4 cm.

B402 Italian peasants at a fountain. Signed »Nerly«. 40,5 × 50,2 cm.

Oehme, Ernst Friedrich

Born Dresden 1797, died ibid. 1855.

B134 View of a Gothic church. Probably painted 1824 in Rome. 49,7 × 40,5 cm.

Onofri, Crescenzio

Born Rome 1632, died Florence 1698.

B31 Landscape. 95,5 × 139,3 cm. Attribution.

B32 Landscape. 95,5 × 139,3 cm. Attribution.

Oppenheim, Moritz

Born Hanau 1800, died Frankfurt-on-Main 1882.

B135 The return of Tobias. Signed »M. Oppenheim. Firenze MDCCCXXIII«. Painted on wood. 64,1 × 76,5 cm.

Orizonte,

See Bloemen, Jan Frans van

Ottesen, Otto Diderich

Born Broager 1816, died Copenhagen 1892.

B280 Still life with fruit. Signed »O. D. Ottesen 1842«. 28,2 × 36,6 cm.

B281 A luncheon table. Signed »O. D. Ottesen 1844«. 39,2 × 33,4 cm.

Overbeck, Johann Friedrich

Born Lübeck 1789, died Rome 1869.

B136 The Virgin and Child. Painted on wood, 1818. 65,8 × 47,1 cm.

Dep. 3 The Good Shepherd. Painted on wood; probably in the 1860s. 36 × 24 cm. Lent by the Ny Carlsberg Glyptotek.

Pacetti, Michelangelo

Born Rome 1793, died after 1855.

B86 The Posillipo Grotto at Naples. Copy of a painting by G. B. Bassi. 47,1 × 36,6 cm.

B401 View of the Tiber in Rome, showing St. Peter's and the Castle of St. Angelo. Signed »M. Pacetti Roma 1835«. 41,5 × 54,5 cm.

Paggi, Giovanni Battista, after

B15 Venus and Cupid. Copy of a painting by G. B. Paggi in the Palazzo Bianco, Genoa. Painted on copper. 10,9 × 9,1 cm.

Perugino, Pietro, after

See Blunck B34.

Petzholdt. Ernst Christian Frederik (Fritz)

Born Copenhagen 1805, died Patras 1838.

B282 Landscape near Veii. Signed »F. Petzholdt. Roma 1835«. 68 × 89,5 cm.

Pietrocola, Floriano

Born Vasto 1809, died Sorrento.

B426 Portrait of Thorvaldsen. Painted on paper. Oval. 14 × 11,5 cm. Presented to the Museum 1892.

Pinturicchio, School of

Italy, around 1500.

B5 The Virgin and Child. Copy of a painting by Pinturicchio in the National Gallery, Washington D. C., Cat.No. 141. Painted on wood. 36,6 × 27,5 cm.

Plagemann, Carl Gustav

Born Södertälje 1805, died Rome 1868.

B176 A nun in her cell. Signed »PL«. Painted on wood. 44,8 × 36,6 cm.

Pontormo, Jacopo, after

B6 The Virgin and Child with the young St. John the Baptist. Copy of a painting by Pontormo in the Uffizi, Florence, Cat.No. 4347.

Painted on wood, probably in the late 18th or early 19th century. 109,9 × 86,3 cm.

Prestel, Johann Erdmann Gottlieb

Born Frankfurt-on-Main 1804, died Mainz 1885.

B137 Stag in a wood. Signed »J. G. Prestel Rom 1835«. 74,5 × 99,8 cm.

Pseudo–Pier Francesco Fiorentino

Florence, late 15th century.

B3 Virgin and Child with two cherubs. Compare a painting ascribed to Pier Francesco Fiorentino in the National Gallery of Art, Washington (Kress Collection K402). Tempera on wood. 70,6 × 54,9 cm. Attribution.

Raphael, after

B303 Copy of a head in Raphael's fresco of »Heliodorus driven out of the Temple« in the Vatican. Painted on ivory. 3,9 × 5,2 cm.

B304 Copy of a head in Raphael's fresco of »Heliodorus driven out of the Temple« in the Vatican. Painted on ivory. 4,3 × 4,6 cm.

B305 Copy of a head in Raphael's fresco of »Heliodorus driven out of the Temple« in the Vatican. Painted on ivory. 4,7 × 4 cm.

See also: Blunck, D. C., B35; Eggers, C., B36; Eggink, J. L., B38; Cades, G., B39.

Rebell, Joseph
Born Vienna 1787, died Dresden 1828.

B138 The Isle of Capri. Signed »Jos. Rebell 1820«. 45,1 × 66,7 cm.

Reinhart, Johann Christian
Born Hof 1761, died Rome 1847.

B139 Forest scene. Signed »C. Reinhart ad nat. f. 1793«. 73,2 × 98,1 cm.

B140 View of the gardens of the Villa Borghese, Rome. Probably painted 1793. 71,9 × 98,1 cm.

B141 View of the Ponte Lupo on the River Anio near Tivoli, in the foreground a youth playing the lyre. Signed »C. Reinhart f. Roma 1823«. Painted on wood. 38,6 × 52,3 cm.

B142 Scene from the Roman Campagna, Torre del Quinto. Signed »C. Reinhart Roma 1823«. Painted on wood. 47,7 × 63,4 cm.

B143 Italian landscape with a hunter (self-portrait). Signed: »C. Reinhart Roma 1835«. 45,1 × 58,8 cm.

Reinhold, Heinrich
Born Gera 1788, died Rome 1825.

B145 Landscape, with the Good Samaritan. Signed »H. Reinhold f. 1823«. 38,6 × 52,3 cm.

B146 Landscape, with Hagar and Ishmael. Signed »Reinhold f. 1823 Roma«. 48,4 × 59,5 cm.

B147 View of St. Peter's from the gardens of the Villa Doria Pamphili, Rome. Signed »Reinhold f. 1823«. 36,6 × 48,8 cm.

B413 Scene from the Isle of Capri. Painted on wood, c. 1823. Unfinished 47 × 66,3 cm.

Richardt, Carl Johan
Born Brede 1816, died Copenhagen 1887.

B283 Portrait of a sailor holding a pipe. Signed »C. Richardt 1839«. 62,8 × 49,1 cm.

Richardt, Joachim Ferdinand
Born Brede 1819, died Oakland, California, 1895.

B284 A studio at the Academy of Fine Arts, Copenhagen. Painted c. 1839. 41,9 × 47,1 cm.

B285 Thorvaldsen in his studio at the Academy of Fine Arts, Copenhagen. Signed »F. Richardt 1840«. 44,5 × 57,5 cm.

Richter, Johann Heinrich
Born Coblenz 1803, died ibid. 1845.

B148 Portrait of the model Fortunata Segatori from Subiaco. Signed »J. Richter f. Roma 1833«. 74,5 × 62,8 cm.

B149 Roman woman with tambourine. Signed »J. Richter f. Roma 1834«. 68 × 56,2 cm.

Riedel, August

Born Bayreuth 1799, died Rome 1883.

B150 A Neapolitan fisherman and his family. Signed »A. Riedel 1833«. 75,9 × 100,7 cm.

B151 Girl bathing. Signed »Riedel f. 1837«. 65,4 × 47,1 cm.

Riepenhausen, Johannes

Born Göttingen 1789, died Rome 1860.

B152 Venus and Adonis. Signed »J. Riepenhausen«. 81,7 × 61,5 cm.

B153 Cupid instructing two young girls. 62,2 × 49,7 cm.

B154 Bramante presenting Raphael to Pope Julius II. Signed »J. Riepenhausen«. Probably painted 1836. 49,7 × 62,2 cm.

B155 A second-hand bookseller in a Roman street, in the background the Temple of Mars Ultor and the Arco di Pantano. Signed »J. Riepenhausen«. 49,1 × 66,2 cm.

Robert, Léopold

Born La Chaux-de-Fonds 1794, died Venice 1835.

B92 The Church of San Paolo fuori le mura the day after the fire of 1823. Replica of a painting from 1824 in the Musée d'Art et d'Histoire, Neuchâtel. Signed »L^{ld} Robert Roma 1825«. 102 × 82,4 cm.

B93 A young Greek sharpening his dagger. Signed »L^{ld} Robert Roma 1829«. 49,1 × 41,9 cm.

Roed, Jørgen

Born Ringsted 1808, died Copenhagen 1888.

B417 Portrait of the painter Albert Küchler (Fra Pietro). Signed »Albert Küchler. Malet i Rom 1862 af J. Roed«. 59,5 × 46,7 cm. Presented to the Museum 1863.

Romanelli, Giovanni Francesco (?)

Born Viterbo c. 1610, died ibid. 1662.

B28 Apollo wearing a laurel wreath. 68 × 49,7 cm. A very tentative attribution.

Rubby, John James

Born Plymouth 1750, died Rome 1812.
See Catel, B299.

Rugendas, Johann Moritz

Born Augsburg 1802, died Weilheim 1858.

B302 Tropical landscape (South America ?) by moonlight. 22,2 × 30,8 cm. Attribution.

Rørbye, Martinus Christian

Born Drammen 1803, died Copenhagen 1848.

B286 View of Athens from the south-west. Signed »Athen M. Rørbye 1836«. 51 × 78,5 cm.

B287 Harbour scene. Palermo. Signed »M. Rørbye 1844«. 83,7 × 125,5 cm.

Salvi, Giovanni Battista (Sassoferrato)

Born Sassoferrato 1609, died Rome 1685.

B16 Praying Virgin. 49,1 × 37,2 cm. Presented to Thorvaldsen by Pope Pius VII.

Sassoferrato,

Se Salvi, Giovanni Battista

Scarsella, Ippolito (Scarsellino), after

B12 A halt during the Flight into Egypt. Copy of a painting ascribed to Scarsellino in the Galleria Nazionale, Parma, Cat.No. 374. Painted on copper. 29,4 × 24,1 cm.

Schack, Sophus Peter Lassenius

Born Copenhagen 1811, died ibid. 1864.

B288 Children singing in a courtyard, winter. Signed »S. S. 1838«. 36,5 × 29,2 cm.

Schadow, Wilhelm

Born Berlin 1788, died Düsseldorf 1862.

B156 The Road to Calvary. Painted on wood. 30,1 × 41,9 cm.

Schedoni,

see Schidone, Bartolomeo

Schick, Gottlieb

Born Stuttgart 1776, died ibid. 1812.

B157 Heroic landscape, with Hagar and Ishmael (?). Probably painted 1803-04. 87,6 × 116,4 cm.

B158 Heroic landscape, with Ruth and Boas. The landscape in the middle distance and background is the work of J. A. Koch. Probably painted 1803-04. 87,6 × 116,4 cm.

Schidone, Bartolomeo, after

B43 The Virgin and Child with the young St. John the Baptist. Copy of a painting by Schidone in the collection of Denis Mahon, London. 47,1 × 35,3 cm.

Schilbach, Johann Heinrich

Born Barchfeld a.d. Werra 1798, died Darmstadt 1851.

B159 View of the Forum Romanum towards the Capitol. Signed »J. H. Schilbach Rom 1825«. 45,1 × 60,2 cm.

B160 View from the Capitol, looking towards the Forum Romanum. Signed »H. Schilbach Roma 18(26)«. 46,5 × 60,8 cm.

Schleisner, Christian Andreas

Born Lyngby 1810, died Copenhagen 1882.

B289 A shoemaker's shop, apprentices poking fun at their master. Signed »C. Schleisner 1838«. 58,8 × 51,7 cm.

Schorn, J.

Active at the beginning of the 19th century.

B446 Portrait of Count Wlod-zimierz Potocki. Signed »Schorn Pinxit«. Gouache. 20,1 × 17 cm.

Seidler, Louise

Born Jena 1786, died Weimar 1866.

B440 Portrait of Fanny Caspars. Signed »Luise S.«. Painted 1819. 74 × 60,5 cm. Presented to the Museum 1937.

Senff, Adolf

Born Halle 1785, died Ostrau 1863.

B161 An antique terracotta vase with flowers. Signed »Adolfo Senff. 1828«. 47,1 × 36,6 cm.

Severn, Joseph

Born Hoxton 1793, died Rome 1879.

B99 Italian woman and her daughter. Signed »I. Severn Rome 1831«. 75,2 × 62,8 cm.

B100 Vintage scene, Italy. Painted on wood, c. 1824. 40,5 × 35,5 cm.

Skovgaard, Peter Christian

Born Hammershus near Ringsted 1817, died Copenhagen 1875.

B450 Nysø on a clear autumn day. Signed »PSkovgaard-1853«. 74 × 112 cm. Bequeathed to the Museum by Rigmor Stampe and Astrid Stampe Feddersen and presented 1974.

Smith, Ludvig August

Born Copenhagen 1820, died ibid. 1906.

B290 The painter J. V. Gertner in his room. Painted c. 1840. 55,2 × 49,7 cm.

Sonne, Jørgen Valentin

Born Birkerød 1801, died Copenhagen 1890.

B291 A battlefield on the morning after the battle. Signed »I. V. Sonne 1833«. 59,5 × 79,8 cm.

B292 Roman country people outside the osteria at Ponte Mammolo. Signed »I. Sonne Roma 1835«. 41,9 × 57,5 cm.

B443 Portrait of Thorvaldsen. Trial section for the frieze on the facade of the Museum. Coloured plaster, c. 1846. 58,8 × 63,6 cm. Purchased 1938.

Steingrübel, Joseph

Born Augsburg 1804, died ibid. 1838.

B162 View of Florence. Signed »J. Steingrübel pinx. Firenze 1834«. 43,2 × 53,6 cm.

Stern, Ignaz

Born Mariahilf c. 1680, died Rome 1748.

B55 Boy blowing soap bubbles. Painted on wood. 60,2 × 94,2 cm.

Stieler, Joseph Karl

Born Mainz 1781, died Munich 1858.

B163 Portrait of Ludwig I of Bavaria. Painted c. 1822. 70 × 51,7 cm.

Storelli, Felix Maria Ferdinando

Born Turin 1778, died Paris 1854.

B85 Italian landscape. Signed »F^d Storelli 1833«. 52,9 × 74,5 cm.

Suhrlandt, Rudolph

Born Ludwigslust 1781, died Schwerin 1862.

B422 Portrait of Thorvaldsen. Replica of B428, painted 1810. 61,5 × 48,5 cm. Purchased by the Museum 1881.

B423 Portrait of Antonio Canova. Painted c. 1812. 62 × 49 cm. Purchased by the Museum 1881.

B428 Portrait of Thorvaldsen. Signed »R. Suhrlandt pin. 1810«. 61,9 × 49 cm. Presented to the Museum 1921.

Taddeo di Bartolo

Born Siena 1362/63, died ibid. 1422.

B2 Predella with, from left to right: Mary Magdalene, Christ in Gethsemane, The Crucifixion, the Resurrection, St. Catherine of Alexandria. Probably painted between 1400 and 1405. Tempera on wood. 17,7 × 145,1 cm.

Teerlink, Abraham

Born Dordrecht 1776, died Rome 1857.

B102 Landscape with cattle. Signed »Teerlink f.«. 30,1 × 41,9 cm.

B103 Italian landscape. Painted on wood. 35,3 × 48,4 cm.

Thöming, Ferdinand Christian Friedrich

Born Eckernförde 1802, died Naples 1873.

B293 A Danish corvette. Signed: »Thöming«. 28,2 × 36,6 cm.

B294 American brig at anchor in the Bay of Naples. Signed »Thöming pinx. Napoli 1827«. 49,7 × 77,2 cm.

B295 The Bay of Naples, Thorvaldsen and Thöming are seated in the nearest fishing-boat with other travellers. Signed »Sorent 1828. F. Thöming«. 51 × 75,9 cm.

B296 View of the coast of Capri near Marina Piccola. Signed »F. Thöming pinx. 1829«. 45,8 × 80,5 cm.

B297 The Blue Grotto, Capri. Signed »Thöming pinx. 1833«. 13,1 × 21,5 cm.

B298 Surf at the coast of Capri. 43,2 × 58,8 cm.

Tischbein, Carl Wilhelm

Born Dessau 1797, died Bückeburg 1855.

B164 Neapolitan fisherman's daughter. Painted between 1816 and 1818. 61,5 × 52,3 cm.

Titian,

See Tiziano Vecellio

Tiziano Vecellio, after

B18 The Virgin and Child with the young St. John the Baptist. Copy of a painting ascribed to the School of Titian in the Uffizi, Florence, Cat. No. 967. Painted on copper. 21,5 × 17 cm.

B40 The education of Cupid. Copy of a painting by Titian in the Galleria Borghese, Rome, Inv.No. 170. 119 × 189,6 cm.

B41 Reclining Venus. Reduced copy of a painting, »Venus from Urbino«, by Titian in the Uffizi, Florence, Cat. No. 1437. 25,5 × 31,4 cm.

Törmer, Benno Friedrich

Born Dresden 1804, died Rome 1859.

B403 Woman from Procida. Signed »Toermer Rom 1833«. 34 × 46,7 cm.

Venetian School

16th century.

B11 Portrait of a Lady. 74,5 × 60,2 cm.

Vernet, Horace

Born Paris 1789, died ibid. 1863.

B94 Portrait of an Armenian priest. Signed »HVt 1830«. 62,2 × 50 cm.

B95 Portrait of Thorvaldsen modelling the bust of Vernet. Signed »Horace Vernet à Son Illustre ami Torwaldsen Rome 1833«. 99,8 × 75,2 cm.

Verschuir, Lieve

Born c. 1630, died Rotterdam 1686.

B48 Seascape. Signed »L. V.« Painted on wood. 17,7 × 22,9 cm. Attribution.

Verstappen, Martin

Born Antwerp 1773, died Rome 1853.

B104 A roadside chapel between Albano and Ariccia. 35,3 × 48,4 cm.

Vogel von Vogelstein, Carl Christian

Born Wildenfels 1788, died Munich 1868.

B425 Portrait of Thorvaldsen. Signed on the back »Carl Vogel pinx. Roma 1815«. 108 × 78,5 cm. Purchased 1890.

Voogd, Hendrik

Born Amsterdam 1766, died Rome 1839.

B56 Italian landscape. 25,5 × 37,2 cm. Attribution.

Wächter, Eberhard
Born Balingen 1762, died Stuttgart
1852.

B165 Portrait of the painter
J. A. Koch. Painted between 1795
and 1798. 29,4 × 22,9 cm.

Weller, Theodor Leopold
Born Mannheim 1802, died ibid.
1880.

B166 Street performers in the Piazza
Montanara, Rome. Signed »18
TW29 Roma«. 69,3 × 88,3 cm.

West, William Edward
Born Lexington, Kentucky, 1788,
died Nashville 1857.

B449 Portrait of Thorvaldsen. 68,5
× 55,5 cm. Presented to the Museum 1972.

Williams, Penry
Born Merthyr Tydfil 1798, died
Rome 1885.

B101 A shepherd-boy and a girl in
the Roman Campagna, in the back
ground Aqua Claudia. Signed
»Penry Williams Rome 1842«. 78,
× 61,5 cm.

Wittmer, Johann Michael
Born Murnau 1802, died Munich
1880.
B167 Æsop seated on a plinth abov
a spring, telling his fables to the
people. Signed »M. Wittmer
F. Romæ 1841«. 73,2 × 107,9 cm.

Zeuthen, Christian Olavius
Born Kastrup 1812, died Copenhagen 1890.

B431 The courtyard of the Thorvaldsen Museum. Signed »Zeuthen
1847«. Painted on paper. 19,9 ×
25,5 cm. Purchased 1924.

Illustrations

List of illustrations

56. Hylas and the Water Nymphs (A484)
57. Nessus and Deianira. Pen drawing, 1814
58. Adonis. Pen drawing, 1837-38
59. Night. Pen drawing, 1815
60. The Lion of Lucerne. Pen drawing, 1814
61-91. Paintings
61. Lorenzo Monaco: B1
62. C. A. Jensen: B432
63. Horace Vernet: B95
64. H. D. C. Martens: Dep. 18
65. Friedrich Nerly: B133
66. J. F. Richardt: B285
67. C. W. Eckersberg: B217
68. Peter Cornelius: B113
69. Heinrich Reinhold: B147
70. Friedrich Overbeck: B136
71. J. A. Koch: B128

72. J. Chr. Reinhart: B143
73. Vincenzo Camuccini: B67
74. Franz Catel: B111
75. Penry Williams: B101
76. Th. L. Weller: B166
77. Léopold Robert: B93
78. P. A. Chauvin: B88
79. Ippolito Caffi: B64
80. Luigi Fioroni: B78
81. Wilhelm Marstrand: B258
82. D. C. Blunck: B199
83. C. W. Eckersberg: B209
84. Wilhelm Bendz: B197
85. Constantin Hansen: B220
86. Martinus Rørbye: B286
87. J. Th. Lundbye: B253
88. P. C. Skovgaard: B450
89. Dankvart Dreyer: B208
90. Jens Juel: B238
91. J. L. Jensen: B232

1

2

3

4

6

7

8

9

11

13

14

15

16

17

18

19

20

24

25

27

28

29

30

31

32

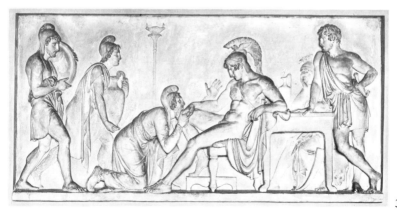

33

34

35

36

39

43

45

46

47

48

49

50

51

52

53

54

55

56

57

58

59

60

61

64

65

66

THORVALDSENS ANKOMST OG MODTAGELSE PAA KIOBENHAVNS RHED DEN 17 SEPT: 1838.

67

68

69

70

71

72

73

74

75

76

77

78

79

80

81

82

83

84

85

86

87

88

89

90

91

Index

Thorvaldsen's works (titles abridged)

Jude (Thaddaeus): A 94(S),
A 105(S), A 106(SM), A 107(SM)
Judgement of Solomon: A 554(R)
Juliane Sophie: A 202(B)
Juno, Cupid asks Jupiter and J.:
A 393(R), A 394(R), A 878(R)
Jupiter, Cupid asks J. and Juno:
A 393(R), A 394(R), A 878(R)
Jupiter, Cupid on J.'s eagle:
A 377(R), A 381(R), A 385(R),
A 386(R)
Jupiter, Ganymede with J.'s eagle:
A 44(S), A 45(S), A 733(S)
Jupiter, Cupid writes the laws of J.:
A 391(R), A 392(R)
Jupiter, Diana and J.: A 345(R)
Jupiter, Minerva, and Nemesis:
A 316(R)
Jupiter, Nemesis and J.: A 320(R),
A 324(R)
Jupiter's eagle bringing Psyche
water: A 443(R)
Justice, Genius of J.: A 531(R)
Justice, Personifications of J. and
Strength: A 609(R)
Justitia: A 549(R)

Knudtzon, Hans Carl: A 231(B)
Knudtzon, Jørgen von Cappelen:
A 230(B)
Kossakowski, Stanislaw: A 295(B),
A 706(B)
Krause, Mrs. von: A 244(B)

Labouchère, Henry: A 294(B)
Lady, Seated: A 168(SM),
A 169(SM)
Lady with a boy, Seated: A 170(SM)
Lambertenghi, Count Luigi Porro
L. and his children: A 619(R)
Latona, The flight of L.: A 458(R)
Lawly, Tomb of Lady Jane:
A 623(R)
Leda and the Swan: A 423(R)

Lion, Dying (the Lucerne Lion):
A 119(S)
Lion, Recumbent: A 121(S),
A 122(S)
Loewy, Jacob: A 885(B)
Louise Augusta: A 818(M)
Lucerne Lion: A 119(S)
Ludwig I: A 232(B), A 233(B)
Luke: A 577(R), A 581(R),
A 583(R), A 584(R)
Luther, Martin: A 160(SM),
A 188(B)
Lyre: A 707(F), A 708(F)
Løffler, Ernst Heinrich: A 630(M),
A 864(M)

Madsen, Hans M. and Johan
Rantzau: A 603(R)
Mahon, Charles James Patrick:
A 286(B)
Maitland, Thomas: A 258(B)
Man, Seated: A 81(SM)
Man on horseback: A 872(R)
Man and wife in Heaven: A 620(R)
Manhood-Autumn: A 640(R),
A 644(R)
Marie Sophie Frederikke: A 192(B),
A 860(B)
Mark: A 576(R), A 580(R)
Mars and Cupid: A 6(S), A 7(S)
Mars, Venus, M., and Cupid:
A 420(R)
Matthew: A 87(S), A 88(SM),
A 575(R), A 579(R)
Maximilian I: A 127(SM), A 128(S),
A 189(B)
Medicine, Genius of M.: A 541(R)
Melanchton, Philipp: A 161(SM)
Meleager and the Calydonian Boar:
A 474(R)
Melpomene: A 331(R)
Mercury: A 5(S), A 868(SM),
A 873(S)

Names